Best Practices in Reading

Improved Performance

LEVEL C

Options
Publishing Inc.

Table of Contents

Best Practices in Reading
Level C

Product Development: Course Crafters, Inc.

Design and Production: The Quarasan Group, Inc.

Cover Design: The Quarasan Group, Inc.

Reviewer: Barbara Block, Director of Literacy and Social Studies
District 11, Bronx, New York

Editors: Jennifer DePino, Carolyn Thresher

Production Supervisor: Sandy Batista

Vice President, Editorial: Christine McArtor

Acknowledgments:
pp 68-70 "Washington" From KIDS DISCOVER's September 2000 issue: Washington, © 2000, Kids Discover, 149 Fifth Avenue, New York, NY 10010. All Rights Reserved. Reprinted by permission of the publisher.

pp 138-140 "Looking Back at Space Station History" From ODYSSEY's January 2000 issue: Open House for the Space Station, © 2000, Cobblestone Publishing Company, 30 Grove Street, Suite C, Peterborough, NH 03458. All Rights Reserved. Reprinted by permission of the publisher.

ISBN 1-56936-825-2

Options Publishing, Inc.
P.O. Box 1749
Merrimack, NH 03054-1749
TOLL FREE: 800-782-7300 ● FAX: 866-424-4056

www.optionspublishing.com

All Rights Reserved. Printed in USA.

15 14 13 12 11 10 9

Getting Ready

DANGEROUS STORM

Alex wants to stay cool on this hot, sticky day. But are those black clouds in the distance bringing danger?

Think About Genre

One genre (ZHON-ruh), or type of literature, is fiction. Fiction stories are stories that are made up by authors. They are made up, but they may tell stories that could really happen. That is true for this adventure story, "Dangerous Storm."

What do you think happens in an adventure story? Fill in the bubble beside each sentence that you think fits an adventure story. You may fill in more than one.

- (A) It is exciting.
- (B) The adventures never happen in real life.
- (C) It is silly.
- (D) The characters face danger.

Think About the Topic

Read the introduction to "Dangerous Storm" again. Ask yourself: *What kinds of storms are dangerous?* Write two kinds of storms below.

1. _____

2. _____

Think Ahead

Look at the story. Read the title and look at the pictures. What do you think "Dangerous Storm" will be about? Write your ideas below.

_____

_____

Strategies:

QUESTION
MAKE INFERENCES
UNDERSTAND GENRE
VISUALIZE

DANGEROUS STORM

QUESTION

Sometimes asking yourself questions as you read a story helps you understand the story better.

> Where are Alex and Grandpa? They are fishing. It took them awhile to get back to shore. They must be in a boat on the lake.

What does Grandpa mean by "got out of the lake just in time"?

_____

_____

_____

hailstones
(HALE-stohnz) small round pieces of ice that fall like rain

"I don't like the look of that sky," said Grandpa. "Let's head home."

"Can't we stay here at the lake and let the rain cool us off?" asked Alex.

The weather was hot and sticky. Fishing in Grandpa's boat was the best thing to happen all day.

"I think we're in for quite a storm," Grandpa said.

By the time they reached shore, a breeze was stirring the air. Suddenly, a flash of lightning ran across the sky. Then they heard loud thunder.

"I'd say we got out of the lake just in time!" said Grandpa.

"Yeah," Alex agreed. He knew it was dangerous to be in the water during a thunderstorm.

The sky looked black. Grandpa's old truck bumped along the gravel road. Before they reached the highway, hailstones were beating down everywhere.

"It's not safe to be on the road," said Grandpa. "Let's head for Aunt Lou's."

Aunt Lou lived on a farm just outside of town. As they pulled into her driveway, Alex saw a strange, dark, V-shaped cloud.

"Tornado!" shouted Grandpa as he jumped from the truck. "Head for the cellar. I've got to help Lou!"

Leaning on her cane, Aunt Lou called from her porch. "Where's Lady, my dog?"

"I'll get her," said Alex. "I saw her go into the shed."

Lady was Aunt Lou's German shepherd. Alex ran toward the shed. Two voices called him back, but he didn't hear them.

Just then the shed door flew off and sailed up. The wind roared like a jet plane. There was no time to run back into the cellar. The tornado was here!

MAKE INFERENCES

Sometimes the author doesn't tell you everything. Use what the author does tell you and what you already know to figure something out.

Why does Grandpa say, "head for the cellar"? I think that must be a safe place during a tornado.

Why did the adults call Alex back?

cellar (SEL-er) a room that is below ground

tornado (tor-NA-do) a violent windstorm

UNDERSTAND GENRE

(adventure story)
When Alex is in the cellar, the author tells you about the dangerous storm. This helps make an adventure story exciting. Two words the author uses to make the storm sound dangerous are

_____

and _____ .

VISUALIZE

Sometimes you have to make a picture of the story in your head to understand the story better. What does Aunt Lou's yard look like in the story? Draw what you see below.

Alex thought fast. He remembered an old root cellar next to the shed. It was like a small cave.

"Here, Lady," he called. "Come with me!" He pulled the big dog out of the shed and into the cellar. Lady was shaking.

The storm crashed and roared over their heads. Alex gently stroked Lady's fur.

Then the wind became quiet. Alex looked out. He stared, surprised. The shed was gone! Aunt Lou and Grandpa were coming toward him.

They could not believe what the tornado left behind. Aunt Lou's porch was in ruins. Power lines were down. Broken boards, tree branches, and smashed flowerpots lay everywhere in her yard.

"You've got a lot of damage here, Lou," said Grandpa.

Aunt Lou just smiled. "We're all safe," she said. "That's what really matters!"

DANGEROUS STORM

Visualize

In this story, the characters need to find an answer for the problems they face.

   Look back at the story to find the information you need to complete this story map.

Title: _____

Characters: _Grandpa_ _____ _____ _____

Problem	Solution
A storm is coming.	Grandpa and Alex leave the lake.
The weather is too dangerous for driving.	
Aunt Lou is looking for her dog.	
Alex cannot get back to Grandpa and Aunt Lou.	

DANGEROUS STORM

Summarize

You can tell a friend what a story was about by giving a summary.

Write a short summary of "Dangerous Storm." Tell how the characters solved some big problems. Include problems and solutions from page 9.

_____

_____

_____

_____

_____

> A summary is short, so I will tell only the most important things in the story. I will tell them in order, from beginning to end.

Determine What Is Important

When you summarize a story, you tell only the most important things. You leave out many smaller details that are part of the story.

Read each sentence below. Fill in the bubble beside the two best sentences to include in a summary of this story.

Ⓐ Grandpa's pickup truck is old.

Ⓑ Grandpa and Alex see a tornado coming.

Ⓒ Lady is a German shepherd.

Ⓓ Alex runs to the shed to get Lady.

Ⓔ Power lines are down in Aunt Lou's yard.

Getting Ready

Some people say that tornadoes are the worst weather on Earth. You will learn about these violent storms and why they are so dangerous.

Think About Genre

The story "Dangerous Storm" is fiction. Another genre, or type of literature, is nonfiction. Nonfiction tells about real people, places, and things. "Tornadoes" is a nonfiction story, or article.

In nonfiction articles, writers help readers understand new information. For example, short sections with headings help readers see important parts of what the article is about.

Quickly look over this nonfiction article. What do you see that helps a reader? Fill in each bubble that tells what you see.

Ⓐ photographs or pictures that look real

Ⓑ large type that shows sections

Ⓒ maps or diagrams to help you understand

Think About the Topic

Read the introduction to "Tornadoes" again. Ask yourself: *What did I learn about tornadoes from reading the adventure story,"Dangerous Storm"?* Write one thing you learned on the lines below.

_____

_____

_____

Think Ahead

Now that you have read the title and looked at the article, think about what you saw. Make a prediction. Write one question that you think this article will answer.

_____

_____

Tornadoes

MAKE CONNECTIONS
Authors sometimes connect new information to ideas that you already know about.

> The author compares a tornado to a funnel. I've seen a funnel, so now I know the shape of a tornado.

Find another comparison the author makes. How does it help you understand tornadoes?

_____

_____

column (KAL-um) something long and upright

funnel (FUN-ul) a tube that is wide at the top and narrow at the bottom

Think about a storm so strong that it can:
- pick up a school bus and carry it through the air.
- suck large trees up out of the ground and throw them about like toys.
- move a house to a different place.

Tornadoes really are that strong!

What is a Tornado?

A tornado is a very strong windstorm. Tornadoes are often called "twisters." This is because a tornado is a twisting column of air. The air is shaped like a funnel. When it touches the ground, it acts like a vacuum cleaner. It sucks dirt and objects up into the air.

Why are Tornadoes so Dangerous?

The wind around the funnel of a tornado reaches speeds of up to 300 miles per hour. Tornadoes have the fastest winds of any storm on Earth. They destroy almost everything in their path.

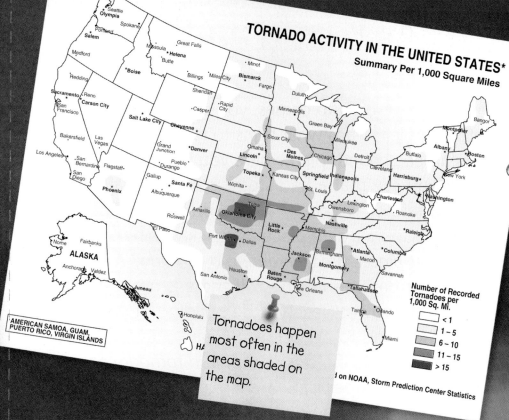

TORNADO ACTIVITY IN THE UNITED STATES*
Summary Per 1,000 Square Miles

AMERICAN SAMOA, GUAM, PUERTO RICO, VIRGIN ISLANDS

Tornadoes happen most often in the areas shaded on the map.

Number of Recorded Tornadoes per 1,000 Sq. Mi.

- < 1
- 1 – 5
- 6 – 10
- 11 – 15
- > 15

...d on NOAA, Storm Prediction Center Statistics

QUESTION
As you read, ask yourself questions to see if you can figure things out.

Why did the author write about both hurricanes and tornadoes? Maybe some people mix up these two kinds of storms.

Do many tornadoes happen in your state? Explain how you came up with your answer. (Notice the map above.)

_____

_____

_____

_____

When and Where Do Tornadoes Happen?

Tornadoes usually begin inside thunderstorms. They can happen in any season of the year. Most tornadoes occur during the spring and summer. They can also happen in any state in the United States. They most often occur in the Midwestern and Eastern states. One part of the Midwest has so many tornadoes, it is known as "Tornado Alley."

Is a Hurricane the Same as a Tornado?

Tornadoes and hurricanes are both whirlwinds. One difference between the two storms is that hurricanes are much larger than tornadoes. A hurricane may be hundreds of miles wide!

Here are some other ways they are different. Hurricanes begin over oceans. They grow slowly and last for many days. Tornadoes do not last long, but they have much faster winds.

whirlwinds
(WURL-winds) air that is spinning and twisting very fast

© 2002 Options Publishing Inc.

I can find out what to do before and during a tornado to make sure I stay safe.

What should you do before a tornado comes? Write down two things.

1. _____

_____

2. _____

_____

If there is a tornado while you are at school, follow your teacher's directions.

What Can You Do to Stay Safe in a Tornado?

Before a tornado comes, you should do two things. First, learn what signs to look for in the weather. Second, plan where you will go for shelter.

If you see that a bad storm is on the way, listen to a radio or watch TV to find out more. Don't panic. Go to a safe place as quickly as possible.

What places are safe during a tornado? A storm cellar or basement is best. If there is no basement, go to the lowest level of the building. If you are at school, go to an inside hallway.

What places are unsafe during a tornado? Stay out of a big open space, such as a gym. Stay away from windows where there may be flying glass. Stay away from power lines. A car is not a safe place either.

A tornado is scary, but you can stay safe if you know what to do.

TORNADO DANGER SIGNS

- Sky turns greenish black
- Air is very still
- Dark funnel-shaped cloud appears
  These are just three possible signs of a tornado coming.

© 2002 Options Publishing Inc.

Tornadoes

Visualize

The chart below is a Venn Diagram. It is a good way to see how hurricanes and tornadoes are the same or different. Reread the section with the heading that asks, "Is a Hurricane the Same as a Tornado?" Then, finish the chart by filling in each part with one of the following words or phrases. The first two are done for you.

- whirlwind
- develops over the ocean
- doesn't last long
- hundreds of miles across

- can be dangerous
- lasts for many days
- fastest winds of any storm

Trees can be torn out of the ground by a tornado.

Tornado | Both Tornado and Hurricane | Hurricane

fastest winds of any storm

hundreds of miles across

Summarize

After you read a nonfiction article, you may want to try to summarize it.

Summarize the section that tells how hurricanes and tornadoes are the same and how they are different. Use the chart from page 15 to help. Write your summary below.

> First I will write the heading "Is a Hurricane the Same as a Tornado?" Next, I will tell how hurricanes and tornadoes are the same. Then I will tell how each is different.

_____

_____

_____

Determine What Is Important

Each section of this article begins with a question. Then it is followed by information to help answer the question. This helps you see what is most important in the article. Read the article again. What is the most important detail of each section? Finish the sentences below. The first one is done for you.

1. Read the first heading, **What is a Tornado?** It tells you that it is important to

know: what a tornado is._____

2. Read the next heading, **Why are Tornadoes so Dangerous?** It tells you that it

is important to know: _____

3. Read the last heading, **What Can You Do to Stay Safe in a Tornado?** It tells

you these important things: _____

_____

Make Connections

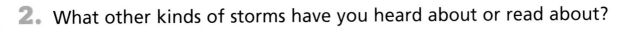

Think about the two selections you just read. Do they remind you of other things you have read, heard, or seen somewhere?

1. What kinds of storms have happened in your city?

_____

_____

2. What other kinds of storms have you heard about or read about?

_____

_____

3. Give two examples of what can happen in a tornado.

_____

_____

4. How can you tell that the characters in "Dangerous Storm" had learned how to be safe in a storm?

_____

_____

Weather forecasters help predict exact locations of storms.

Putting **Fiction And Nonfiction Together**

DANGEROUS STORM Tornadoes

Write a Plan of Action

Write two things you need to do to stay safe if you hear a tornado warning. You may also want to tell what you should NOT do next to number 3.

1. _____

2. _____

3. _____

BLACKLINE MASTER Before you write, use the Blackline Master your teacher will give you to plan your action plan.

Plan Your Research

You have read about tornadoes and about other dangerous storms. Write two questions you still have about tornadoes or other bad storms. Use the questions to start your research. How will you find the answer to each question?

1. _____

_____

2. _____

_____

Net Connection

http://www.fema.gov/kids/tornado.htm
http://whyfiles.org/013tornado/tornadomain1.html
http://www.txdirect.net/~msattler/thist.htm

Getting Ready

The Field of Freaky Flowers

It can't be easy being an insect. Just about every creature on Earth is bigger. Some plants can even mean danger—as you'll discover in this "freaky" fantasy story.

Think About Genre

In fiction, the stories are made up. Some can seem real, and some can never happen. Fantasy is a special kind of fiction. Impossible things can happen in a fantasy. Animals might talk. Or plants might dance. Anything you can imagine can happen in a fantasy.

Fill in the circles next to two things that could happen only in a fantasy.

Ⓐ Spiders play guitars.

Ⓑ The dog gets lost.

Ⓒ A boy is two inches tall.

Ⓓ Thunder booms.

Think About the Topic

Read the above introduction to "The Field of Freaky Flowers" again. Ask yourself: *Why might some plants mean danger for an insect?* Write two ideas on the lines below.

1. _____

2. _____

Think Ahead

Look through the story. Then look at the title and illustrations. What do you think you will read about in "The Field of Freaky Flowers"?

_____

_____

_____

Strategies:
VISUALIZE
MAKE INFERENCES
UNDERSTAND GENRE
QUESTION

VISUALIZE:

The writer gives details about how the fantasy characters look and what they do. The details help you picture them.

> Ma Dragonfly shakes her antennas at her kids the way a human mom shakes her finger.

What details help you imagine Red and Lucky?

antennas (an-TEN-uhs) long feelers on the head of an insect

recited (re-SITE-ed) said aloud from memory

The Field of Freaky Flowers

Red and Lucky sat on a log at the edge of the swamp. Ma Dragonfly fluttered over the log. They'd all been arguing. "I know you boys want to go fishing by yourselves," Ma Dragonfly said. "I just don't know whether you two are ready to go alone."

"WE'RE READY!" they shouted together.

"Then prove it," she said, shaking her antennas at them. "Tell me my three rules."

Red and Lucky wiggled their wings impatiently. Then they recited the rules. "*One:* Fly straight. *Two:* Don't talk to the ducks. *Three:* Stay away from the Field of Freaky Flowers."

"Okay boys! You can go," Ma said.

But Ma Dragonfly still worried. As her boys flew off, she shouted after them. "DON'T FORGET! STAY AWAY FROM THE FIELD OF FREAKY FLOWERS. IT'S DANGEROUS!"

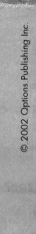

Soon Red and Lucky saw the pond sparkling below. They zipped over its clear surface, catching one water flea after another. They found mosquito eggs, too.

"YUM! YUM! YUM!" they both said, many times.

Lucky and Red fished and ate, fished and ate, fished and ate. Soon their fish bags were full. They knew they should head home to Ma Dragonfly.

"Have you ever seen the field of freaky flowers?" Red asked Lucky.

"No, have you?" Lucky replied.

"Of course not. But I wonder what it looks like."

"Are you thinking the same thing I'm thinking?"

Soon the two dragonflies were flying as fast as their wings could carry them—straight to the field of freaky flowers.

"Those yellow flowers look like pitchers," said Red.

"Those green plants look like clams," added Lucky. They both laughed.

"They don't look dangerous at all!"

"Not one bit."

MAKE INFERENCES
Sometimes story characters surprise us. Look for clues in the story. Try to figure out why characters act the way they do.

I know why Red and Lucky didn't go right home. They were having too much fun.

Why didn't Red and Lucky follow Ma Dragonfly's rules about the field of freaky flowers?

pitcher (PICH-er) a container with a spout

UNDERSTAND GENRE

(fantasy story)
Remember, in fantasy stories impossible things happen. What part of this fantasy story is made up?

_____

_____

_____

QUESTION

Ask yourself questions as you read. This helps you understand the story better. Think, <u>W</u>ho? <u>W</u>hat? <u>W</u>hen? <u>W</u>here? and <u>H</u>ow? Here's an <u>H</u> question: How did Lucky get into trouble?

Write a <u>W</u> question.

Question: _____

_____

_____

_____

_____

A moment later, Lucky flew over a yellow plant shaped like a jug. "Bet there are some delicious fleas in there. I'll take a peek."

So Lucky landed on it.

"What do you see, Lucky?" Red asked.

"Nothing yet," he answered, and then—he fell in! "HELP!" he shouted.

"What's wrong?" Red yelled.

"It's sticky in here. AHHHH!"

Red flew over the yellow plant. "I'm coming in," he said.

"Don't!" shouted Lucky. "You'll just get stuck."

Just then, Red spotted a long piece of thick grass. He pulled it out of the ground, flew over to the plant, and slipped it inside.

"What's that?" called Lucky from down below.

"It's a grass rope. Grab on," Red said. "I'll pull you out." And that's just what Red did.

Then the two dragonflies were happily on their way home, and they never ever visited the field of freaky flowers again!

delicious (de-LISH-us)
yummy, tasty

The Field of Freaky Flowers

Visualize

Most stories have a problem that gets solved in the end. Think about "The Field of Freaky Flowers." The problem is *Can Red and Lucky go out on their own and get home safely?* In the story map below, the problem is filled in. So are the settings, or where the story takes place. Look back over the story to help you fill in the rest of the map.

Title

_____

Characters

_____

_____

Settings

swamp, pond, field of freaky flowers

Problem

Can Red and Lucky go out on their own and get home safely?

Important Events

_____

Solution

_____

The Field of Freaky Flowers

Summarize

A good summary is a short retelling of the story that includes the most important events and leaves out details that are not as important.

Imagine that you are Red or Lucky. What would you tell your friends about your adventure? Use the story map on page 23 to help you remember the most important things that happened.

_____

_____

_____

> I think I'll be Red, so I'll start with, "Ma let Lucky and me go fishing." Then I'll tell where we went and what happened.

_____

_____

Determine What Is Important

Figuring out what's important helps to make a good summary. If you leave out a detail, and it does not change the story, then the detail is probably not very important and should not be in the summary. It may be very interesting, but that's not enough. Decide which sentences below tell important parts of the story. Put an ✗ in front of each sentence that is _not very important_ and would not be part of a summary.

_____ Red and Lucky are two young dragonflies.

_____ Ma Dragonfly decides to let Red and Lucky go fishing.

_____ Red and Lucky love eating water fleas.

_____ The mosquito eggs taste great.

_____ Red and Lucky decide to go to the field of freaky flowers.

_____ One plant is shaped like a pitcher.

Getting Ready

Dragonflies don't really talk about freaky flowers. But some plants really *are* dangerous for insects and spiders. In this science article, you can read the story of these plants. It's stranger than fiction!

Think About Genre

In a fantasy story, a writer uses imagination. A fantasy may have strange, made-up creatures and events. In nonfiction, the information is real and is not made up. Nonfiction writers give facts to help you think about information. Some of the facts—like those in this science article—can be pretty strange!

Look over "Plants with Traps." Fill in the bubble for each thing that helps you know an article is nonfiction instead of fiction.

Ⓐ It has photographs.

Ⓑ It has a title.

Ⓒ It has a diagram.

Ⓓ It gives facts.

Venus' flytraps

Think About the Topic

Read the introduction to "Plants with Traps" again. What did you read in "The Field of Freaky Flowers" that might be true? Complete the following sentence.

Plants can be _____

_____

Think Ahead

You already looked over the science article to see how you could tell it is nonfiction. Predict two things you think you might learn about plants with traps.

1. _____

_____

2. _____

_____

Reading Nonfiction

Strategies:

QUESTION
UNDERSTAND GENRE
MAKE CONNECTIONS

QUESTION

Turning the headings of a science article into a question can help you understand what you read.

> I can turn the first heading into a question: What should insects beware of? Some plants can kill insects.

Rewrite the second heading as a question. Then answer it.

_____

_____

_____

_____

dewdrops (DO-drops) little drops of water

species (SPEE-sheez) kinds or types of plants or animals

Insects, Beware!

A fly buzzes over a tiny green plant called the sundew. The sundew plant sparkles. It seems to be covered with dewdrops. It smells sweet. The fly lands on the plant. Now it's in trouble!

The fly's feet stick to the plant. The fly tries to escape, but the little hairs of the plant bend and trap it. The fly becomes food—for the sundew plant.

Types of Insect-Eating Plants

The sundew is an insect-eating plant. Sometimes insect-eating plants are called carnivorous. [car-NIV-er-us] This word means "meat eating." There are about 450 different species of insect-eating plants. They are found on all the continents—except for the frozen region of Antarctica.

These plants have different colors, shapes, sizes, and smells. They come in green, yellow, red, and even purple. They range in size from less than one inch to about two feet tall.

Sundew plants are usually less than one inch tall.

All insect-eating plants only grow in wet areas. These are floating bladderworts.

Plants with Traps

These kinds of plants can't chase their prey. Because they don't have legs or wings, their prey must come to them. Like other plants, insect-eating plants have colors and smells that attract insects. Some of these plants also eat small animals, like frogs or even mice. One example of an animal-eating plant is the bladderwort, which dines on tiny water animals.

To catch their food, animal-eating and insect-eating plants have traps. Some are *moving traps* and some are *still traps*.

- **Moving traps** have parts that clamp, swing, open, or close. Sundew plants have moving traps. So do bladderworts and Venus' flytraps.
- **Still traps** don't move. Instead, the plants ooze sticky glue or slippery goop. Pitcher plants have still traps.

UNDERSTAND GENRE
(science article)
This science article explains how animal-eating plants catch their prey.

Now I understand how animal-eating plants attract insects—with smells or colors.

Animal-eating plants trap their food in two ways. What are they?

1. _____

_____

2. _____

_____

clamp (KLAMP) close shut

prey (PRAY) a living thing which is food for another living thing

The writer compares insect-eating plants to things you know. This helps you get a better understanding of the plants.

A Venus' flytrap is compared to the shape of a clamshell. Also, it snaps shut like a clamshell.

The writer compares the shape of a pitcher plant to a thin jug. What do you think that would look like? Draw a picture of a pitcher plant.

One Example of a Moving Trap

The Venus' flytrap is the most well-known of all insect-eating plants. White flowers grow on it in the spring. But the plant's leaves are its traps. Each leaf is shaped like a clamshell. Along the curved edge are stiff bristles. Touching the bristles inside the trap causes the two sides of the leaf to snap shut. Juices flow from the leaf. These juices break down the insect's body for the plant to use for food.

One Example of a Still Trap

The pitcher plant is shaped like a thin jug. The inside walls of this plant have slippery hairs or waxy goop. Insects lose their footing and slip down. . . down . . . down. Some pitcher plants have water in the bottom. The insects drown. Other pitcher plants make juices to kill their prey.

bristles (BRIS-ulz)
stiff hairs

1 Open clamshell leaf with bristles

2 An insect lands and sets off the trap

3 The insect is trapped inside the Venus' flytrap

©2002 Options Publishing Inc.

Plants with Traps

The last page of this article has two headings. Each one tells about a kind of insect-eating plant.

Use the word web below to identify important information about the two kinds of plants. Some words have been filled in for you. Find other helpful words about each kind of plant in the article.

moving

Venus' Flytrap

clam-shaped trap

_____

_____

Insect-eating Plants

jug shape

Pitcher Plant

juices kill prey

_____

_____

Summarize

A summary is a brief retelling of
what you read. It can cover
a whole article or just one part.
If you summarize only one part,
you include details from that part.

Summarize the last section of "Plants with Traps."
Use the word web on page 29 to help you.

My summary will start with
the name of the section and
explain what it is about. Then it
will describe the two examples
of insect-eating plants.

_____

_____

_____

Pitcher plant

Determine What Is Important

Any science article includes main ideas as well as
details. Main ideas are the most important ideas.
Details are often facts or pieces of information that
writers use to explain each main idea. Read each
group of facts below. Then fill in the bubble next to
the sentence in each group that is the main idea.

1. Ⓐ Animal-eating and insect-eating plants
   have traps.

   Ⓑ These plants have parts that swing, clamp, or snap.

2. Ⓐ The sundew is an insect-eating plant.

   Ⓑ There are about 450 kinds of insect-eating plants.

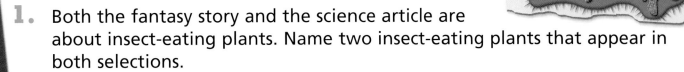

Make Connections

Think about the two selections you just read. Did reading about insect-eating plants make you think of any garden you've ever seen?

1. Both the fantasy story and the science article are about insect-eating plants. Name two insect-eating plants that appear in both selections.

_____

_____

2. Many animals eat plants. Do you think it seems strange that some plants eat animals? Why or why not?

_____

_____

3. Which insect-eating or animal-eating plant trap is the most interesting to you? Why?

_____

_____

4. There are many meat-eating animals. Name two.

a. _____

b. _____

Write an Opinion

Do you think it would be good to have a garden with insect-eating plants? Write your opinion (what you think) in a complete sentence. Then support your opinion by explaining why you think this way. Give one good reason.

Opinion: _____

Reason: _____

BLACKLINE MASTER Before you write, use the Blackline Master your teacher will give you to write your opinion.

Plan Your Research

With a partner, brainstorm a list of the plants you know. Then choose one plant you want to learn more about. Write two questions you would like to find answers to. Each of you can pick one question to work on.

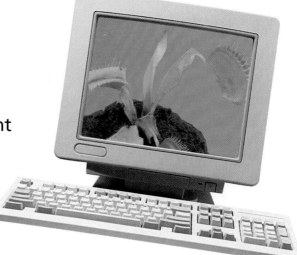

1. _____

_____

2. _____

_____

Net Connection

http://www.carnivorousplants.org
http://www.webschooling.com/scimisc1.html

THE SUPER SANDWICH MAKING MACHINE

Anna's neighbor is an inventor.
When one of his inventions won't work, can Anna save the day?

Think About Genre

It is easy to tell that fictional stories of fantasy are made up because strange things happen—plants can talk or dogs can drive cars. Other stories of fiction seem like real life. The characters and events seem real. Such stories are called realistic fiction.

Which one of these statements is true about a realistic fictional story? Fill in the bubble beside it.

(A) It is always a kind of fantasy.

(B) It seems like it could really happen.

(C) The events could not happen in real life.

Think About the Topic

You can tell from the introduction that the story you're going to read is about an inventor and an invention. Do you know about any famous inventors? Can you think of any interesting inventions? Write what you know about inventors or inventions on the lines below.

_____

_____

Think Ahead

Take a quick look at the story. Read the title and look at the pictures. What kind of invention or inventions do you think you might find in this story?

_____

_____

Strategies:
UNDERSTAND GENRE
VISUALIZE
QUESTION
MAKE INFERENCES

The Super Sandwich Making Machine

UNDERSTAND GENRE
(realistic fiction)
When you start reading a story, you may not know if it is realistic or fantasy. Look at the characters for clues to help you decide.

At first, I thought Mr. Makit might be a fantasy character. But he invents realistic things.

In real life, how would this invention be helpful?

Anna lived in a triple-decker—a three-story house with one apartment on each level. Her family lived on the second floor. Anna loved living there. She said, "We're like the filling of a sandwich—the best part."

Her friend Alan lived upstairs with his grandparents. Downstairs was the amazing Mr. Makit.

Mr. Makit was an inventor. He was a short, round man with bright eyes and a cloud of fuzzy gray hair. His inventions were not grand things like rockets. They were **gadgets** to solve everyday problems.

Mr. Makit's latest invention was a cat feeder with a timer on it. He didn't like to stop working to feed his cat. Now his invention took care of that.

"With a little imagination, you can solve any problem," he liked to say.

gadget (GAJ-it) a small tool or machine made to do a certain task

Mr. Makit had once helped Anna solve a problem. Her brother kept going into her room and taking her things without asking. Mr. Makit helped Anna invent an alarm for her door. It really worked!

Some of Mr. Makit's inventions didn't work quite so well—like the one he was working on now.

"This is supposed to be a sandwich-making machine," he told Anna.

Anna saw a messy pile of bread, cheese, and lettuce next to Mr. Makit's machine.

"So far it has only made a mess!" he groaned. "And I promised Open Table that I would bring them 200 sandwiches by five o'clock today."

Open Table gave meals to people who did not have enough to eat. Anna thought it was great that Mr. Makit wanted to help. She could see that he had already bought all the ingredients for the sandwiches.

She had an idea.

VISUALIZE

How do you think Mr. Makit's sandwich-making machine works? Picture it in your mind. Tell about it or draw it below.

QUESTION

As you read, ask yourself questions about things that are not clear. You may find the answers later on.

I'm not clear about Open Table. What is it?

Read on to find the answer. Write it on the lines.

ingredients
(in-GREED-ee-ents)
parts that are used to make something

MAKE INFERENCES

Anna does not tell Mr. Makit exactly what she plans to do. Instead, the author gives you a set of clues. The clues help you infer, or figure out, what is happening.

How do you think Mr. Makit feels about Anna's "machine"?

_____

_____

_____

What clues helped you figure this out?

_____

_____

_____

_____

_____

_____

beamed (BEEMD)
looked bright, happy

"Guess what!" said Anna. "I'm inventing a sandwich-making machine, too. I think it will solve the problem. Wait here while I get it."

Soon she returned with her mother and Alan.

Anna lined the food up on the table. Then her invention went into action. First, Alan put cheese on a slice of bread. Then Anna's mother added more fillings and another slice of bread. Mr. Makit cut the sandwich in half. Anna slid the halves into a sandwich bag.

They passed sandwich after sandwich down the line. Soon 200 sandwiches were ready to go.

Anna and Mr. Makit rushed to Open Table. After they delivered the sandwiches, Mr. Makit sighed with relief. Then he smiled at Anna.

"You know what I've always said," he beamed. "With a little imagination, you can solve any problem!"

© 2002 Options Publishing Inc.

Visualize

THE SUPER SANDWICH MAKING MACHINE

The main character in this story is Anna. Read the words in the box below. Choose two words that you think describe Anna. Use these words to complete the character web below.

On each sandwich, write a word that describes Anna. Then write your "support"—evidence from the story that shows this character trait One has already been done for you.

helpful	cheerful	scared
clever	bored	funny
mean	kind	

Anna is

Support:

Anna is

cheerful

Support: She loves where she lives.

Anna

Anna is

Support:

The Super Sandwich Making Machine

Summarize

Pretend that you are Anna. Write a short summary of "The Super Sandwich-Making Machine" the way Anna might tell it. Use these sentence starters to help you. Keep your summary short. Tell only the most important parts of the story.

My name is Anna, and I live with my family in:

_____

Mr. Makit lives in the apartment house, too. He is an inventor, and he has a problem:

_____

I helped solve his problem by:

I'll begin by telling where I live and who the important characters are. Then I'll explain Mr. Makit's problem. Finally, I'll tell how I helped solve the problem.

Determine What Is Important

Sometimes interesting things are not the most important things. Only the most important things should be in a short summary of the story. Read the statements below. Fill in the bubbles beside the two statements that are most important. (You might have used them in Anna's summary.)

Ⓐ Alan lived upstairs.

Ⓑ Mr. Makit was an inventor.

Ⓒ Mr. Makit invented a cat feeder with a timer.

Ⓓ Mr. Makit invented an alarm for Anna's room.

Ⓔ Mr. Makit promised to make 200 sandwiches.

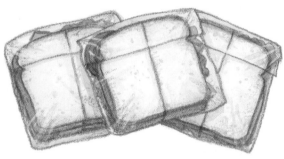

Look through the story. Find one more important idea that you could add to your summary. Write it below.

_____

_____

© 2002 Options Publishing Inc.

Getting Ready

You've read about Mr. Makit, Anna and their inventions. Have you ever thought of a new way to do something? Why not turn your ideas into inventions? This nonfiction article could help you get started.

From Idea to Invention

Think About Genre

Photographs in a nonfiction article often give you important information. What do the photographs show you about the article you will be reading?

_____

_____

Captions are the words that go with photographs. They help you understand the photographs. In this article you will see photographs with captions. Notice how the captions help you.

Think About the Topic

Reread the introduction to "From Idea to Invention." Ask yourself: _What would I like to find out to help me with inventing?_ Complete the following sentence.

When I read this article, I hope to learn

_____ .

Think Ahead

After looking at the photographs, captions, and headings, what do you expect to read about? Fill in the bubble next to the description that you think best fits "From Idea to Invention."

Ⓐ information about famous inventors of the past

Ⓑ true stories about young people who have invented things

Ⓒ directions for how to invent a new tool

Ⓓ funny stories about inventions that failed

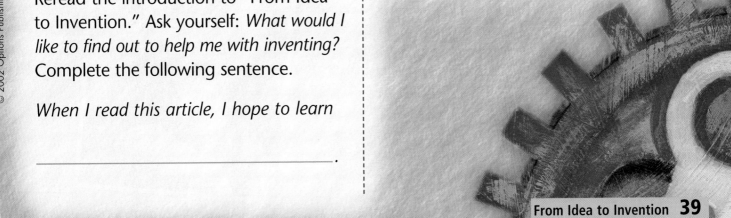

From Idea to Invention

MAKE CONNECTIONS
Try to connect what you read to something in your own life.

The caption makes me wonder about our school playground. Does it welcome all children, or just able-bodied children?

How are playgrounds you have used like the ones that Matthew helps design? How are they different?

able-bodied
(AY-bul-bah-deed) able to do what most people can do

disabled (dis-AY-buld)
not able to do certain things

navigate
(NAV-uh-GAYT) guide the way

In the Swing

For Matthew Cavedon, the playground wasn't much fun. Because he uses a wheelchair, there wasn't much to do. That's why he designed a swing that can hold wheelchairs.

"It is real simple!" says Matthew. "I like boats and I like swings. Other kids do, too! The glider boat swing I dreamed up lets kids navigate the high seas together."

Matthew called his swing "The Dreamer." It was a great success. Matthew now helps design playgrounds where disabled and able-bodied children have fun playing together.

Matthew Cavedon helps design playgrounds that welcome all children.

These sisters have made it fun to learn manners. That takes imagination!

Kids' Play

Kaitlin and Kelley Kennedy didn't like their etiquette class. Their mother said they could stop going if they figured out a better way to learn manners. The girls invented a board game called "Jungle Etiquette." Players answer etiquette questions to move around the board.

It took the girls two years to design the game. They had to learn a lot about good manners to do it. Now they are glad their game can teach others.

Making the World Better

Ashley Mulroy is an "Aqua Hero." She tested the water of the Ohio River. She also tested the water supply in Wheeling, West Virginia, her home town. She found traces of medicine in the water.

Medicine gets into water in many harmless ways. People pour old medicine down the drain, and it goes through the water pipes. Farm animals get medicine, and when their pens are washed, the water soaks into the ground. Ashley's project won a prize. Now other scientists are checking the water for traces of medicine.

UNDERSTAND GENRE
(nonfiction article)
This article tells about different kinds of inventions and discoveries.

The headings tell me what to expect in each section. They tell me what the author thinks is important.

You learn about an invention and a discovery on this page. What do the headings tell you about the difference between them?

_____

_____

Ashley's good questions have led to some important answers.

aqua (AK-wuh) water

etiquette (ET-ih-ket) rules for polite ways to behave

pens (PENZ) places where animals are kept

traces (TRAYS-iz) small amounts

QUESTION

Think about Ryan Schroeder's invention. What questions would you like to ask Ryan about it?

_____

_____

_____

_____

_____

_____

_____

Getting Started

Ryan Schroeder lives on a farm that raises hogs. He saw that hogs' waste can be a big problem. The waste flows off farm fields into streams and causes water pollution.

Ryan also noticed another problem.

When a new house is built, the leftover drywall is thrown away.

Ryan invented a way to soak up hogs' waste with pieces of drywall. This means less waste going into the water, and less drywall being thrown away, too!

Other programs also encourage young people to invent. Every year, many students enter inventions in national science contests. One recent winner invented a "Rescue Tube" that could help save the life of a person who has fallen through the ice.

When kids start inventing, they come up with great ideas!

Ryan Schroeder is working on a pollution solution.

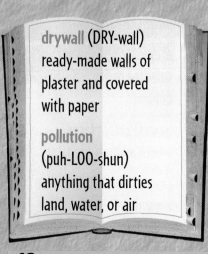

drywall (DRY-wall) ready-made walls of plaster and covered with paper

pollution (puh-LOO-shun) anything that dirties land, water, or air

From Idea to Invention

Visualize

The author of this article points out ways in which the inventions are the same and ways in which they are different. Use this chart to help organize what you know about the inventions. For each invention, place a check mark under each description that fits that invention.

	Fun	Invented or discovered by a young person	Helps people	School project
Matthew Cavedon's "The Dreamer"				
Kennedy Sisters' "Jungle Etiquette"				
Ryan Schroeder's "Pollution Solution"				
Ashley Mulroy "Aqua Hero"				

What is the same about all four inventions or discoveries?
(Hint: Notice which column has check marks in all four boxes.)

_____

From Idea to Invention

Summarize

A brief summary tells what an article is mainly about. It gives the main idea and the most important ideas that follow it. It does not give details.

Complete each sentence below. The finished sentences will be a short summary of "From Idea to Invention."

> I've thought about how the inventions in the article are alike. That helps me figure out the main idea. I'll start my summary with the main idea.

1. "From Idea to Invention" is mainly about _____

_____

2. The first three parts tell about _____

_____

3. The last part tells about _____

_____

Determine What Is Important

Think about the main idea of the article. The most important ideas are the ones that best support the main idea.

Read each pair of sentences below. Fill in the bubble beside the sentence that best supports the main idea.

> Invent America is one of many groups that help kids with inventions.

(A) Matthew Cavedon likes boats and swings.
(B) Matthew Cavedon designs playground equipment.

(C) The Kennedy sisters thought up a board game.
(D) The Kennedy sisters didn't like their etiquette class.

(E) Ryan Schroeder lives on a farm.
(F) Ryan Schroeder is working on a pollution solution.

INVENT AMERICA!® 2000
bringing bright ideas out of young minds

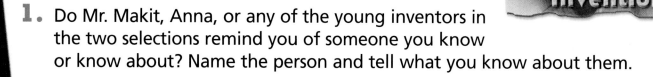

Make Connections

Think of the inventors and discoveries you have read about in "The Super Sandwich-Making Machine" and "From Idea to Invention."

1. Do Mr. Makit, Anna, or any of the young inventors in the two selections remind you of someone you know or know about? Name the person and tell what you know about them.

_____

_____

2. Do you think it is important for inventors to know a lot about science? Explain why or why not.

_____

_____

THE DAYTON WRIGHT AIRPLANE. FAIR FIELD. MAY 14-18

The airplane was invented in 1903 by the Wright brothers in Kitty Hawk, North Carolina.

3. How is Anna's invention in "The Super Sandwich-Making Machine" like some of the inventions in "From Idea to Invention"? How is it different?

_____

_____

4. Describe an idea that you have for an invention. Tell why people might need it or have fun with it, or both.

_____

THE SUPER SANDWICH MAKING MACHINE

From Idea to Invention

Write Directions

Think of something that you use often—
something simple like a backpack or a drinking straw.
Pretend that you have just now invented it. Imagine
that no one else knows how to use it yet. On the lines
below, explain what the invention is for, and write
directions for using it. Then draw a diagram of it to help people understand.

_____

_____

_____

BLACKLINE MASTER Before you write, use the Blackline Master your teacher
will give you to help you plan and draw your invention.

Plan Your Research

Have these selections made you think
about inventing something? Think of a
problem you might solve or a person you
could help by making an invention. Make
a list of questions that you need to answer
to start on your invention.

_____

_____

_____

Net Connection

http://www.amazing-kids.org/kids3-00.htm
http://www.inventamerica.com/
http://www.boundlessplaygrounds.org/

Journey of Wonder

Do you know there are places in the world that were not built by people? Nature put them there. Amazing! They are called "natural wonders." Imagine taking a birthday trip to a natural wonder–200 years ago!

Think About Genre

All stories of fiction are made up. Some of them use real facts from long ago to tell a story. These stories are called historical fiction. Both real and made-up characters tell a story about real events in history.

Fill in the bubble that best tells what you find in historical fiction.

Ⓐ All events are true.

Ⓑ Real and made-up characters tell a story about real events in history.

Ⓒ All events are make-believe.

Think About the Topic

Read the introduction to "Journey of Wonder" again. It gives you an idea of what a natural wonder is. Look at the four places listed below. Three of the four are natural wonders. Only one was built by people, so it is not a natural wonder. Fill in the bubble of the one that is **not** a natural wonder.

Ⓐ Arizona Painted Desert

Ⓑ Grand Canyon

Ⓒ Empire State Building

Ⓓ Mount Everest

Think Ahead

Take a quick look at the story. Read the title and see the pictures. Write two things you think will be in the story "Journey of Wonder."

1. _____

2. _____

Strategies:
MAKE INFERENCES
QUESTION
UNDERSTAND GENRE
VISUALIZE

Journey of Wonder

MAKE INFERENCES

Sometimes authors give clues through what the characters say.

Mama says Jenny is "up before the rooster." Roosters crow at dawn, so Jenny got up before dawn.

Papa gives Jenny clues to where they're going. List one clue.

At last, the big day had arrived. Jenny Burke pulled her **bonnet** over her brown curls, then raced to the kitchen. Her mother was stirring **porridge** over the fire in the **hearth**. "You're up before the rooster!" Mama said.

"Yes, Mama," Jenny replied. She was too excited to sleep. She was going on a trip with Papa—a surprise for her ninth birthday.

After breakfast, Papa and Jenny put blankets and food in the wagon. Then they set off.

"Where are we going, Papa?"

"I'll give you a hint," said Papa. "We're traveling north from Tonawanda, then west."

Three years ago Jenny's family moved to Tonawanda, New York. Papa had a supply store near their cabin.

"Are we going to visit my cousins in Canada?"

"You'll find out soon enough," said Papa.

bonnet (BON-et) hat for women or girls

hearth (HARTH) fireplace

porridge (POOR-ij) hot cereal

© 2002 Options Publishing Inc.

The wagon creaked along. The summer sun was hot. They passed many orchards with apple and pear trees.

They came to a low bridge that crossed over a river. The bridge wasn't much wider than the wagon, and the sides were made of rope, not wood. It looked so rickety!

"Are we taking the wagon over *that*, Papa?" Jenny asked.

"We have to!" Papa said. "You'll have to get out of the wagon and walk."

Papa led the horses onto the shaky bridge. Jenny walked ahead of him, hanging on to the rope. She was sure the bridge would fall into the river. But it didn't.

By late afternoon, they reached Black Rock on the Niagara River. They took a ferry across. Then they stopped at an inn for the night.

QUESTION

Ask yourself questions to make sure you know what's happening in a story.

How does Jenny feel about crossing the bridge? I can tell she is worried because she thinks the bridge will fall into the river.

Write a question you have below. Share it with a friend. See if you can answer each other's question.

creaked (KREKT) squeaked

inn (IN) hotel along road

rickety (RIK-uh-tee) weak or shaky

After dinner at the inn, they sat on the porch and felt a cool breeze in the air. Papa pointed to a **misty spray** in the distance. "Over there is your birthday surprise."

He would not say more.

The next morning, a **guide** met them at the inn. He led them along a path near the Niagara River. Jenny heard a loud, powerful pounding. She thought of the town **blacksmith** hammering iron horseshoes. This sound was like a million blacksmiths hammering at once!

They climbed a high hill. They saw the river falling over a cliff shaped like a gigantic horseshoe. They saw the great Niagara Falls! A giant rainbow curved above the shaking, turning waters. Mist rose up and wet their faces.

Everything was so beautiful! Jenny turned to Papa and grinned. What a wonderful birthday surprise!

blacksmith
(BLAK-smith) person who makes or fixes things made of iron, like horseshoes

guide (GIED) person who shows the way

misty spray
(MIS-tee spray) tiny drops of water in the air

© 2002 Options Publishing Inc.

Visualize

Stories have a beginning, a middle, and an end. Think about "Journey of Wonder." Use the story map below to tell about important things that happen in each part of the story. One important event is already filled in for each part. Write the story title and one more important event in each box. Go back to the story for ideas.

Journey of Wonder

Title

_____

In the beginning

Jenny is excited about going on a trip for her birthday.

_____

_____

In the middle

Jenny and Papa came to a bridge.

_____

_____

Finally, in the end

A guide leads them to the falls.

_____

_____

Journey of Wonder

Summarize

A summary tells the main events of a story.

Think about "Journey of Wonder." Choose the best summary below. Use your story map on page 51 to help you decide.

Ⓐ Jenny and her father go on a trip. It is summer time. It is Jenny's birthday. They have fun.

Ⓑ Jenny was a girl who lived 200 years ago in Tonawanda, New York. Her father owned a store in the town. They had a cabin and a wagon. They crossed a bridge with their wagon.

Ⓒ Jenny and her father leave their home in Tonawanda on a wagon trip. They travel west. They cross a rickety bridge and take a ferry. Then they visit Niagara Falls— a great surprise for Jenny.

> I'll think about what the main characters (Jenny and her father) did in each part of the story—the beginning, middle, and end. That helps me write the best summary.

Determine What Is Important

Read page 50 again. Choose what you think are the four most important things that happen on the page. List them in order as they appear in that part of the story. The first one is done for you.

1. Papa pointed to a misty spray in the distance.

2. _____

_____

3. _____

_____

4. _____

_____

Getting Ready

Jenny thought that Niagara Falls sounded like a million blacksmiths hammering away on horse shoes. What could cause that much noise? Read on and you'll find out.

Thunder of Water

Think About Genre

Historical fiction includes real details or facts from the past. But the characters, actions, places, or events can be made up. That is why it is fiction. Nonfiction tells only about real people, real places, real actions, and real events.

Nonfiction can look different, too. An article may be divided into parts that have titles or headings. These headings tell you what each part is about. Look over the nonfiction article, "Thunder of Water." Then answer these questions:

1. How many headings are there?

_____

2. How many photographs are there?

_____

3. Do you see: a graph? a chart? or a map?

_____

Think About the Topic

Read the introduction to "Thunder of Water" again. Then think about "Journey of Wonder." Write two things that you know about Niagara Falls.

1. _____

_____

2. _____

_____

Think Ahead

You looked at the article, "Thunder of Water." Write two things you expect to learn.

1. _____

2. _____

Thunder of Water

MAKE CONNECTIONS
Nonfiction writers tell about things that are new to readers. They try to connect something new with something you already know.

> The writer uses the idea of bathtubs to explain how much water spills over Niagara Falls.

What idea does the writer use to explain how high Niagara Falls is?

_____

_____

The Greatest Flow on Earth

Think of a million bathtubs full of water. Line up all those bathtubs, and they would reach from New York to Florida. Now think of all that water falling all at once over a tall, wide cliff.

That's how much water spills over Niagara Falls every second. It adds up to 400,000 tons of water per minute. No other waterfall on Earth has so much water flowing over it!

Niagara Falls is about 180 feet high. That's about as tall as a building with 16 floors. In the world, 50 waterfalls are higher. Only one other waterfall is wider. That is Victoria Falls in Africa.

Look at the Great Lakes on the map. These lakes hold much of the world's fresh water. The water passes through Lake Erie, and then moves into the Niagara River—and over Niagara Falls.

fresh water
(FRESH WA-ter) water that is not salty

tons (TUNS) heavy weight

Niagara Falls as seen from the U.S.

© 2004 Options Publishing Inc.

Sieur de La Salle, a French explorer, joined Father Hennepin in exploring Niagara Falls.

The five Great Lakes hold much of the world's fresh water.

Early History of Niagara Falls

The first people to visit Niagara Falls were the Native American Indians. *Niagara* is an Iroquois word meaning "thunder of water."

Early explorers heard stories about a great waterfall. Not many of them saw Niagara Falls. A French priest named Father Hennepin was the first to write about it. In 1678, he joined an explorer in Canada named Sieur de La Salle.

When they reached the falls, Father Hennepin was scared. He wrote about a "horrible mass of water." He told of a "sound more terrible than that of thunder." People were amazed! His books sold very, very well.

After the American Revolution (1763–1783), more settlers arrived in western New York. They built roads along the Native American Indian trails. Many tourists came to visit the wonderful waterfall.

UNDERSTAND GENRE

(article) Nonfiction articles about history tell about events that happen in time order.

The part, "Early History of Niagara Falls," begins with Native American Indians—the first to know about the Falls.

What did an early explorer do to help more people learn about Niagara Falls?

_____

_____

explorers
(ek-SPLOR-ers) people who travel in a place that is not well known

Iroquois
(IHR-eh-kwoy) Native American group who live in the region of Niagara Falls

tourists (TUR-ists) sightseers

Why does water flow slower now? The power plants on the river take away some of the water.

Why has Niagara Falls moved?

_____

_____

_____

eroded (ee-ROHD-ed) worn away

Niagara Falls Today

Every year about 10 million tourists visit Niagara Falls. There are many hotels nearby. Boats bring visitors close to the bottom of the Falls.

Time changes most things. For awhile now power plants have used the river's water to make electricity. This has caused the water to flow more slowly than it did years ago. The Falls have also moved. They are about 2,000 feet farther back from where they were in Father Hennepin's time. That is because over the years water has eroded the rocky cliff.

Even with these changes, Niagara Falls has great beauty and power. It is still a natural wonder to people from all over the world!

Brave spectators view the base of the falls from a boat.

Believe It or Not

In 1860, Blondin, an acrobat, crossed the Niagara River near the falls on a tightrope. Later he put a stove out on the rope. Then he cooked a meal.

© 2002 Options Publishing Inc.

Thunder of Water

Visualize

The last two parts of the article tell about events in the order that they happened. They start with the heading "Early History of Niagara Falls," and end with "Niagara Falls Today."

Look at the chart below. It shows what happened over time. Complete the sentences to show the order of events. The first and last ones are done for you.

The Iroquois Indians lived in and around New York.

Native American Indians were the first visitors.

⬇

In 1678, Father Hennepin and Sieur de la Salle _____

_____

⬇

After the American Revolution in 1783 _____

_____

⬇

Today, 10 million tourists visit the Falls. Power plants use the river's water. The Falls have moved. It still has great power and beauty, and is a natural wonder.

Summarize

When you finish reading an article, you may want to share it with a friend. A summary helps you do that. It should be short and clear. It tells in your own words what the article is about.

Summarize the last two parts of the article. Use your chart on page 57 to help you with the order of events. Use the lines below.

My summary will start by telling what each part is about–the history of Niagara Falls and today.

_____

_____

_____

Determine What Is Important

The headings help you understand the most important information in an article. The first heading is: "The Greatest Flow on Earth." Turn this heading into a question: *What is the Greatest Flow on Earth?* The answer to that question is one important idea of the story.

Turn each heading below into a question. Then answer each question.

A rainbow forms in the mist below the Niagara Falls.

Early History of Niagara Falls

_____

_____

Niagara Falls Today

_____

_____

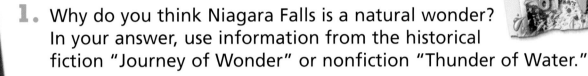

Make Connections

Think about the two selections you read. Did reading about Niagara Falls remind you of a trip you've taken? Did it make you want to travel?

1. Why do you think Niagara Falls is a natural wonder? In your answer, use information from the historical fiction "Journey of Wonder" or nonfiction "Thunder of Water."

_____

_____

2. Was the Niagara Falls Jenny saw in "Journey of Wonder" different from the way it is today? How?

_____

_____

_____

3. Has any place you've read about—or seen— filled you with wonder? Tell about it.

The Grand Canyon is an American natural wonder.

_____

_____

_____

Write a Descriptive Postcard

Pretend you are visiting Niagara Falls. Write a postcard to a friend. Describe what you see and hear at the Falls. Tell your feelings about being there. Use what you learned in both selections. If you have really been there, use your own experience to tell about it.

BLACKLINE MASTER Before you write, use the Blackline Master your teacher will give you to plan your postcard.

Plan Your Research

There are many natural wonders in the world, like the Grand Canyon, Mount Everest, and Niagara Falls. Choose one of these or another that you would like to visit. Write 2 questions you would like to research before you go.

1. _____

2. _____

   _____

Net Connection

http://www.infoniagara.com
http://www.planetpals.com/worldwonders.html

Getting Ready

They Are Patriots

In 1775, the American colonies belonged to Britain—but many Americans hoped to change that. In this historical fiction story, each person has to make a choice. Should they remain loyal to the king? Or should they join the fight for independence?

Think About Genre

Historical fiction stories seem real and take place in the past. To make the story seem real, authors need to know a lot about how people lived during that time in history. Authors who write historical fiction always need to do research and to use their imagination.

How do you know that "They Are Patriots" takes place in the past? Fill in the bubble beside each sentence that tells you.

Ⓐ The characters' clothes and homes fit with that time in history.

Ⓑ Things happen in the story that could not happen in real life.

Ⓒ The story tells about events that really happened in history.

Think About the Topic

Read the above introduction to "They Are Patriots" again. Ask yourself: *Why did some people in the American colonies want to fight for independence?* Write your answer below.

_____

_____

_____

Think Ahead

Take a quick look at the story. Think of what you read in the introduction. What do you think the characters argue about in "They Are Patriots"? Write your answer below.

_____

_____

_____

Reading Fiction

Strategies:
MAKE INFERENCES
QUESTION
VISUALIZE
UNDERSTAND GENRE

They Are Patriots

MAKE INFERENCES

When authors do not tell how their characters feel, they expect you to use clues and what you already know to figure it out.

I can tell Ben's father loves him because of what he says and what I know about family arguments.

What helped me figure this out?

Patriot (PAY-tree-et) supporter of independence from British rule

traitor (TRAYT- er) a person who helps an enemy of his or her own country

Mary heard her father and brother Ben arguing in the hall.

"I'll not live with a traitor under my roof!" her father shouted.

"Then I'll not be staying," replied Ben. With a slam of the door, he was gone.

Mary ran to her father. His face was red with anger. "Fight the British, indeed! That boy has lost his mind."

Mary knew Ben was meeting secretly with people who wanted to be independent from Britain. Most of the men of their town, Concord, Massachusetts, were on her brother's side. They called themselves Patriots.

Mary's father was not one of them. He was loyal to the King of Britain.

"Has Ben left us for good?" asked Mary.

"I hope not," her father sighed. "Perhaps he'll come home soon."

© 2002 Options Publishing Inc.

Mary thought Ben was right. But she didn't think she should say so.

Then, on April 19, 1775, British troops marched out of Boston. They shot and killed Patriots in Lexington and at the North Bridge in Concord.

"This is terrible!" her father roared. "I may soon have to join the Patriots!"

Mary was glad to hear his words. She tried very hard to bring her father over to the Patriots' side.

The town was buzzing with news. The American colonies had joined together to form a Continental Congress. At meetings of the Continental Congress, leaders decided what to do.

Mary listened to all the news. Every day she told her father something bad about the British. Finally, one day in June, her words made a difference.

QUESTION
Ask yourself questions when you wonder about ideas or events. Reread or read ahead to help you find answers.

I wonder, "Why does Mary keep her thoughts to herself?"

Why do you think so?

colonies
(KAHL-uh- neez)
settlements that are far from the nation that rules them

© 2002 Options Publishing Inc.

Authors help us "see" what people look like in our minds.

What words help you picture George Washington? Write them below.

UNDERSTAND GENRE
(historical fiction)
This story is historical fiction. Some events really happened. Name two historical events that led Mary's father to change his mind.

1. _____

_____

2. _____

_____

commander-in-chief
(keh MAN-der-in-cheef)
the person who is in charge at the highest level

Mary knew how much her father looked up to George Washington. Twenty years earlier, they had fought together against the French.

"The Continental Congress named George Washington the commander-in-chief of a new Continental Army," Mary told her father. "He is coming here to help drive the British out of Boston!"

Mary's father was convinced at last.

On July 2, George Washington took command of the army outside Boston. Mary and her father went to Cambridge to see him gallop by. As the tall, handsome man in a blue uniform rode by on his large white horse, people cheered.

Suddenly, Mary heard a voice she knew. She turned, and there was Ben! Mary ran to him and yelled that their father was now a Patriot. "You can come home again, Ben!" Mary cried.

They Are Patriots

Visualize

Think about how the author put this story together.

Look back at "They Are Patriots" to find the information you need to complete this story map.

Title

_____

Characters

_____

_____

Setting

time _____

place _____

Problem

Father is loyal to Britain, but Ben and Mary want him to join the Patriots.

Important Events

_____

_____

Conclusion

_____

They Are Patriots

Summarize

After you read a story, try to think about how one of the characters might tell it. How would Ben tell the story?

Imagine that you are Ben. Write a few sentences in your journal after the parade. You are pretending to be Ben, so remember to use the word "I" as you write your summary.

> I'll imagine that I am Ben. I'll tell why I left home, what the British did, what my sister did, and how my father changed his mind.

_____

_____

_____

_____

Determine What Is Important

This chart tells something that is important in the story and why it is important. On the left, list one more thing that is important. On the right, tell why it is important.

Something Important	Why It's Important
1. Father was loyal to the king.	1. It explains why he was angry with Ben.
2.	2.

Getting Ready

Who is that man on the one-dollar bill? And why is his picture there? Find out about the man we call the "Father of His Country."

Washington

Think About Genre

The story of a real person's life is called a biography (bie-AHG-re-fee). It tells about things that happened in the person's life. A biography is just one kind of nonfiction.

Look at this short biography of George Washington. George Washington lived before we had photography. What kinds of pictures does this article use to help you get a picture of him and his times in history?

_____

_____

_____

Think About the Topic

Reread the introduction to "Washington." Ask yourself: *What do I already know about George Washington? What did I learn about him from reading the story "They Are Patriots"?* Write something you know about George Washington on the lines below.

_____

_____

Think Ahead

Now that you have read the title and looked at the biography, make a prediction. Write two questions you expect to answer by reading this short biography, "Washington."

1. _____

2. _____

★★★★★★★★★★★ Washington ★★★★★★★★★★★

The First President

When George Washington died in 1799, General Henry Lee said that Washington had been "first in war, first in peace, and first in the hearts of his countrymen."

Most people remember Washington as the nation's first president, but he was also an important military leader. He led the nation to victory in the American Revolution, an eight-year fight for independence from Britain.

Washington always tried to be honest and to tell the truth. He also felt a strong duty to help his country. Shy and modest, he never expected to be the nation's first president. Yet, when the nation's leaders told him that his country needed him, he agreed to serve. Luckily for us, George Washington was the right person for the job!

The Growing-up Years

George Washington was born in 1732 at Bridges' Creek in Virginia. He was the oldest of five children. He had a younger sister and three younger brothers. Because his father had been married before, George also had two older half brothers.

MAKE INFERENCES

General Henry Lee said in a speech that Washington was "first in the hearts of his countrymen." What do you think Henry Lee's words mean? Answer in words you could use to tell a friend.

_____

_____

_____

_____

_____

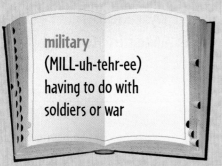

military
(MILL-uh-tehr-ee)
having to do with
soldiers or war

George's home after age 16 at Mount Vernon

When George was 11, his father died. With his father's death, George became closer to his half brother Lawrence. He went often to visit Lawrence's farm, called Mount Vernon. When he was 16, he went to live with Lawrence.

A Military Career

By the time Washington turned 21, two powerful nations, Britain and France, were about to start a war to win control of North America.

Both countries had settlers there. Many British colonists were eager to move west into the Ohio Valley, but the French were determined to keep them out. When at last France and Britain started fighting, George Washington's military career began.

George's Marriage

On January 6, 1759, George Washington married Martha Dandridge Custis, a young widow with two small children. Martha's first husband had been a wealthy Virginia farmer. He had left her money and 17,000 acres of land. With Martha's land and money added to his own, Washington was now a wealthy man.

George's marriage to Martha.

QUESTION
Remember to ask yourself questions about the words and pictures in this article.

What land did George Washington own before his marriage? It must have been Mount Vernon, after Lawrence died.

What questions do you have about Martha Washington? Write one question and try to figure out an answer.

_____

_____

_____

career (kuh-REER) the kind of work someone does to earn a living

The headings on this page connect this part of Washington's biography with the words at the beginning–the words that General Henry Lee spoke when Washington died.

How was George Washington first in war and first in peace?

_____

_____

_____

_____

_____

Famous painting of Washington crossing the Delaware.

First in War: General Washington

After the war with France ended, the British thought the American colonies should pay **taxes** to support the British soldiers who protected them. Also, they wanted the colonies to buy goods from Britain and sell Britain their farm crops. Many colonists **resented** both the taxes and the rules about trade. By 1775, many colonists were calling for independence from Britain. When British soldiers fought colonists at Lexington and Concord, the American Revolution began. America's leaders chose George Washington as commander-in-chief of their newly formed army.

First in Peace: Mr. President

As the nation's first president, Washington had to figure out exactly what his job was. Americans didn't want another king. But what did they want? They decided to have a government by the people and for the people. No other nation at that time had such a government.

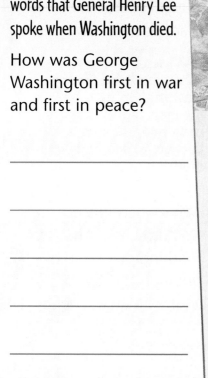

resented
(ree-ZENT-ed) felt angry about

taxes (TAKS-es) money people pay to a government

Visualize

Think about the way information is organized in this short biography. The first part tells you why George Washington was an important person. The rest of the biography tells about important events in Washington's life. The large, blue headings tell you which part of his life story you will read about next.

Use the time line below to list important events in George Washington's life. Be sure to put events in time order. Find the 6 events (including his birth) that you think are most important. Include dates when they are given. One is done for you.

On April 14, 1789, Washington found out that he was elected president. But what were people to call the new president? Some suggested "His Highness" or "His Excellence." Lawmakers settled on "Mr. President."

1799	Washington dies

Summarize

If someone from another country asked you about George Washington, what would you tell him or her?

In three sentences, tell the things that you think are most important to know about this man.

> I will first look at the beginning section that tells why Washington was famous.

_____

_____

_____

_____

Determine What Is Important

A biography usually includes many facts that tell about a person's life. You will remember the facts better when you can understand why they are important.

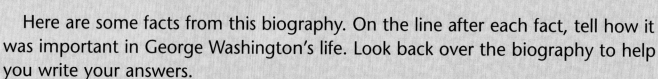

George Washington felt a strong duty to help his country.

Here are some facts from this biography. On the line after each fact, tell how it was important in George Washington's life. Look back over the biography to help you write your answers.

1. When Washington was 21, Britain and France were about to go to war.

_____

_____

2. When British soldiers battled with colonists in Lexington and Concord, the American Revolution began.

_____

_____

They Are Patriots

Washington
★★★★★★★★★★★★★

Make Connections

Think about the two selections you just read. How does one selection help you understand the other? Do they remind you of other things you have read or heard?

1. What did you know about George Washington before you read the two selections? Each selection probably added to what you know. Show this in a chart about your knowledge of George Washington.

What I Have Learned about George Washington

I already knew:

_____

_____

I learned from "They Are Patriots":

_____

_____

I learned from "Washington":

_____

_____

A statue of President George Washington in the George Washington Memorial in Alexandria, Virginia.

2. Which do you like better: reading history or reading historical fiction? Tell why.

_____

Write about an Event

The day that Mary saw George Washington was a special event in her life. Write about a special event in your life. Describe what you saw, felt, and heard.

_____

_____

_____

_____

BLACKLINE MASTER Before you write, use the Blackline Master your teacher will give you to plan your description.

Plan Your Research

What else would you like to learn about George Washington or the American Revolution? Write two questions you would like to have answered.

1. _____

_____

2. _____

_____

Net Connection

http://www.whitehouse.gov/history/presidents/gw1.html
http://www.mountvernon.org/
http://www.si.umich.edu/spies/
http://www.nps.gov/mima/

Getting Ready

Tears and Dreams

Picture yourself moving to a new land. Do you think it would be exciting? In this story, one boy's move turns out to be much harder than he'd ever dreamed.

Think About Genre

Historical fiction is one genre of fiction. In this story, the characters are made up, but the events are real. They come from history.

The story "Tears and Dreams" is historical fiction. What do you think you will find in the story? Fill in the bubble next to each thing.

(A) boats that talk

(B) an event from history

(C) real places

(D) realistic characters

Think About the Topic

Reread the introduction above. Ask yourself: *What would it be like to move to a new land?* Complete the word-web.

```
        scary
          |
   ___  new  ___
        land
          |        exciting
       _____
```

Think Ahead

Look through the story. Think about the introduction and the illustrations. Complete the sentence.

I think this story will tell about:

_____

_____

Strategies:

VISUALIZE
MAKE CONNECTIONS
UNDERSTAND GENRE
MAKE INFERENCES

Tears and Dreams

VISUALIZE

Use the author's words to make pictures in your mind. These mind pictures will help you "see" what is happening in the story.

Mind pictures can help me understand what it was like on the lower deck.

Picture yourself on the lower deck with Chen. Tell what you see.

March 5, 1912

Chen Hung stood on the main deck of the *Golden Eagle*. He had come all the way from Canton, China. At last, the ship entered San Francisco Harbor.

"Isn't the harbor beautiful?" Chen said to his friend, Long Lee.

"It's prettier than I dreamed," Long answered.

"I thought I'd never see the sun again," Chen said.

"Or smell the fresh air," Long added.

Until this morning, Chen had been living on the ship's lower deck. The deck was dark and wet.

The 30-day trip had been hard. Many men got sick. Some days they had no food.

Chen missed his family the whole time. He was the youngest boy on the ship.

Today, he would see his uncle. Chen's uncle had a place where he could stay. He also had a job waiting for Chen. Chen planned to send money back to his family. That's why he came to America.

The ship pulled up to a dock. "We're almost there!" said Long excitedly.

"We will never forget this day!" Chen exclaimed.

"Never!" they repeated together.

A Few Hours Later . . .

Chen found himself waiting in a crowded room. All the men from the lower deck were there, too. They carried everything they owned in packages tied to the ends of long poles. They whispered quietly.

No women were in sight. Mostly, the men from China came without their wives or children. The men were all here to earn money.

On the ship, Chen imagined that his uncle would meet him right away. They would go straight to his new home in San Francisco. That was his dream. But that was not what happened.

"Come this way," shouted an official.

The crowd of men followed him. Soon they were back at the harbor. They all boarded boats.

"Where are we going?" Chen asked an older man he had met on the *Golden Eagle*.

"They are taking us to Angel Island. They will look over our papers there. Then they will let us enter San Francisco," he said. "I hope."

MAKE CONNECTIONS
The writer doesn't tell you how Chen feels. Put yourself in his place. How would you feel?

Poor Chen! He's been on the ship for 30 days. Now he has to wait even longer. I would be so disappointed.

Have you ever been disappointed like Chen? What happened?

official (oh-FI-shul) a person in charge

© 2002 Options Publishing Inc.

此涙仰擁錐
途鎖望夢股
囚旅前一求
困夢擺筆榮
厄天相過別
吾使思重廣
爲島尺洋山

Three Days Later . . .

Chen sat on the lower bunk in a large room. Over his bunk were two more bunks. In all, 100 men—mostly from China—lived in the crowded room.

Chen was glad that he would see his uncle today. The past three days had been very hard.

Doctors gave Chen a complete check-up. Officials asked him question after question. He was scared all the time.

Chen's friend Long sat next to him. Like Chen, Long was meeting *his* uncle today. "Angel Island has been terrible," Chen said, sadly.

"Yes," Long agreed, "but still we are lucky."

On Angel Island, Chen had met men who were waiting for weeks—and even months. Many had written their thoughts on the walls. Chen read them.

"I'll never, ever forget my stay here," said Chen.

"NEVER!" Chen and Long repeated together.

UNDERSTAND GENRE
(historical fiction)
The following story details are true and come from research:
- stack of three bunks
- 100 men in the **barracks**
- writing on the walls

Write one other detail that might come from research.

_____

_____

MAKE INFERENCES
Sometimes you have to figure out what an author is trying to say. Look at the words from the wall at Angel Island. What could a "package of dreams" be? Fill in the bubble next to the best answer.

(A) hopes for the future

(B) a birthday present

(C) a box for sleeping

English words for Chinese writing on a wall at Angel Island.
I left Canton with a package of dreams.
I carried my dreams on a pole across the sea.
I saw the land of hope–but could not enter.
I shed tears on the Island of Angels.
There, I lost my package of dreams.

---

barracks (BER-icks)
a building or many buildings where large groups of people live

© 2002 Options Publishing Inc.

Tears and Dreams

Visualize

In "Tears and Dreams," we learn about the kind of person Chen Hung is through what he says and what he does. These are called character traits. If you understand a character's traits, you will be able to understand a character. Use the character chart below to help you understand Chen Hung. Read each character trait on the chart. Find evidence from the story that shows each trait. Write it on the lines next to the trait.

Chen Hung Character Chart

Character Trait	Evidence
1. brave	1. _____ _____
2. unselfish	2. plans to send money back home
3. patient	3. _____ _____
4. caring	4. _____ _____

Summarize

A story summary tells only the main points of a story. Sometimes you can summarize a story by describing the character and the most important things that happen to him or her.

Write a summary of "Tears and Dreams." Use the character chart on page 79 to help you explain what happened to Chen Hung.

Tears and Dreams

> First I'll tell them who Chen Hung is and where he is going. Then I'll explain what he is like—and the things he goes through.

_____

_____

_____

_____

_____

_____

Determine What Is Important

A story summary should include important ideas and leave out small details. Put a check in front of the most important idea under each story section below.

Section 1: March 5, 1912
Chen came to America on a boat.
Chen came to America to earn money for his family.

Section 2: A Few Hours Later . . .
Chen went to Angel Island first, not to his uncle's.
Chen asked an older friend a question.

Section 3: Three Days Later . . .
Chen knew he was lucky, even though he had a hard time at Angel Island.
Chen sat on the bunk with his friend.

Getting Ready

Chen Hung entered the United States through Angel Island in California. How might his experience have been different if he had come through Ellis Island in New York? Read this article to find out.

Ellis and Angel: Islands of Hope

Think About Genre

Some nonfiction articles about history compare and contrast. They may compare and contrast people, places, or things.

What does it mean to compare two things?

_____

_____

_____

What does it mean to contrast two things?

_____

_____

_____

_____

Think About the Topic

Reread the introduction to "Ellis and Angel: Islands of Hope." Write two things you learned about Angel Island in "Tears and Dreams."

1. _____

2. _____

Think Ahead

This article compares and contrasts Ellis Island to Angel Island. Take a quick look at the headings and photos. What two things do you think will be compared? Fill in the bubbles next to your predictions.

Ⓐ the immigration centers on both islands

Ⓑ jobs for immigrants

Ⓒ both islands today

MAKE INFERENCES

Authors don't always tell you everything. Sometimes they give you clues and you have to think of what you already know to figure out what the author is really saying.

> I think the author is saying that it wasn't so easy coming to America.

The Chinese boy had an even harder stay. How do you know?

Clue _____

_____

---

coast (KOST) land along the sea

ferry (FER-ee) a boat that carries people and cars

immigration (im-ih-GRAY-shun) movement of people to a new land

Ellis and Angel:
Islands of Hope

Starting New Lives

The year is 1910. A young girl from Germany has been at the immigration center on Ellis Island for five days. Doctors have given her a complete check-up. Officials have asked her questions.

At last, she boards a boat for New York City. The girl waves to Lady Liberty—the great statue in New York Harbor. She and her family will start a new life in America.

Meanwhile, on the west coast of the United States, a teenage Chinese boy waits for a ferry. He is finally leaving Angel Island in San Francisco Bay.

The boy has been at the immigration station there for three weeks. Tomorrow he will begin working. He plans to send money to help his family back in China.

Land of Immigrants

The United States is a land filled with immigrants. Some families have just arrived from faraway places. Other families settled here a long time ago.

Young immigrants waiting for medical exams before entering the United States.

For many years, anyone could come to America. Then, after awhile, the United States government began to set limits.

Angel Island

Ellis Island

Ellis Island Immigration Center

In 1892, an immigration center opened on Ellis Island in New York Harbor.

Ships landing in the harbor carried many passengers—rich and poor. Most rich passengers entered the United States quickly. Most poor passengers went by boat or barge to Ellis Island.

Days on Ellis Island

Most people stayed four or five days. They had to fill out forms. Inspectors asked them many questions. Doctors checked their health. After that, most immigrants could enter the country. There were some—about one in 50 people—who were sent back to their home country.

The center was open until 1954. During that time, 12 million people entered the United States through the Island.

Ellis Island Today

In 1965, Ellis Island became part of the Liberty National Monument. Today, the main building is the Ellis Island Immigration Museum. About 2 million people visit this historic place each year.

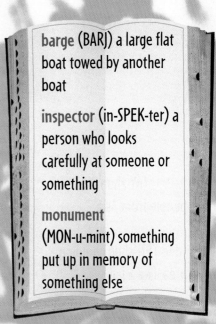

UNDERSTAND GENRE
(nonfiction article)
The article compares and contrasts Ellis Island to Angel Island. This part of the article tells about Ellis Island. There are three headings. Each heading tells what you will be reading about. Write them down.

Heading 1: _____

_____

Heading 2: _____

_____

Heading 3: _____

_____

barge (BARJ) a large flat boat towed by another boat

inspector (in-SPEK-ter) a person who looks carefully at someone or something

monument (MON-u-mint) something put up in memory of something else

Angel Island Immigration Center

In 1910, another United States immigration station opened. This one was in San Francisco Bay, on Angel Island. Some people called it the "Ellis Island of the West."

Inspection Process

Angel Island became a detention center for Chinese immigrants. Most people were kept on the island for two to three weeks. Many stayed for months—or even years.

They lived in crowded places. Most immigrants did not speak English. Officials asked them many questions. It could all be very confusing. About one out of four Chinese immigrants were not allowed into the United States.

In 30 years, more than 250,000 immigrants passed through Angel Island. Most of them were Asians.

Angel Island Today

Immigrants no longer enter through Angel Island. Today, there is a museum in the old station. Visitors come to read poems that immigrants wrote on the walls. They come to learn the story of America's Asian immigrants.

Asians (AY-zhuns) people from Asia
detention (dee-TEN-shun) holding area, like a jail

© 2002 Options Publishing Inc.

Ellis and Angel: Islands of Hope

Visualize

This article compares and contrasts Ellis Island to Angel Island. It explains how the two immigration centers were alike and how they were different.

Fill in the chart below to show how the two islands were similar or different.

Ellis Island

Angel Island

Alike

1. officials asked questions in both places
2. immigrants were sent back home from both places

3. _____

4. _____

Different

1. opened in 1892
2. 1 in 50 sent back

3. _____

4. _____

Different

1. opened in 1910
2. 1 in 4 sent back

3. _____

4. _____

Ellis and Angel:
Islands of Hope

Summarize

Summarizing is a good way to check your memory. It is also a good way to see how much you understand. You should be able to summarize if you:

- remember what you read.
- understand what you read.

Summarize the information in "Ellis and Angel: Islands of Hope." Use the compare-contrast chart on page 85 to help you.

_____

_____

_____

_____

_____

I will start my summary by telling what two places are being compared and contrasted. Next, I'll tell how the two centers were alike. Then, I'll describe their differences.

Determine What Is Important

The headings of each section can tell you what is important in that section. If you turn the heading into a question, it will lead you to the main idea of the section. Circle the questions below that ask about the main idea. There are two.

1. What was Ellis Island Immigration Center like?

2. How many people immigrated to Ellis Island in all?

3. For how many years was Angel Island an immigration center?

4. What is Angel Island like today?

The Statue of Liberty stands for freedom for all who come to America.

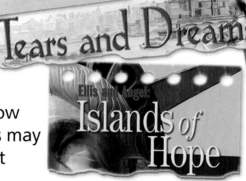

Make Connections

Remember how the two islands are similar, and how they are different. Think about how the selections may be like or unlike other stories you have read about people moving from one place to another.

1. There are many people who still move to the United States today. Why do you think they come here?

_____

2. How was Chen Hung's story like the story of the Chinese boy in the first section of the nonfiction article? How was it different?

Alike: _____

_____

Different: _____

_____

3. Why do you think tourists visit Ellis Island and Angel Island today?

_____

_____

4. Suppose you could speak with Chen Hung. What two questions would you ask?

a. _____

b. _____

Immigrants traveling by boat to America.

Write a Journal Entry

It's 1920. Suppose you just arrived at Ellis Island or Angel Island with your family. Write a journal entry about your experience. Explain what you see, hear, smell, and feel. Tell what happens.

_____

_____

_____

BLACKLINE MASTER Before you write, use the Blackline Master your teacher will give you to help you plan your journal entry.

Plan Your Research

Would you like to visit Chen Hung's homeland? China has many amazing places. Find out about one part of China. How about Canton, Hong Kong, Beijing, or Taiwan? Take your pick. Write three questions you would like to research.

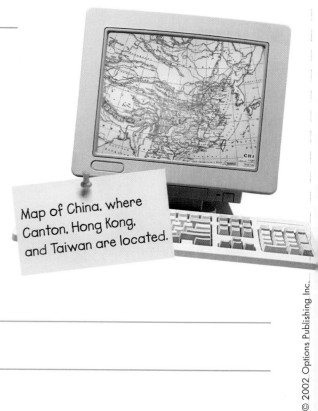

Map of China, where Canton, Hong Kong, and Taiwan are located.

1. _____

2. _____

3. _____

www.angelisland.org
www.ellisisland.org

Getting Ready

Attic ★ ★ ★ Stardust

What would you expect from a visit to the attic? Possibly a treasure hunt? It may become a trip to the past, and a time to learn about people you love! In this story, a visit to the attic is all of those things—and more.

Think About Genre

In realistic fiction, the writer tries to make the story seem real. The characters are like people you might meet. The places are like those you might visit.

What do you expect to find in realistic fiction? Fill in two bubbles.

Ⓐ The characters could live in your town.

Ⓑ The place seems real.

Ⓒ The characters are talking birds.

Ⓓ The place is always a place you know.

Think About the Topic

Read the introduction to "Attic Stardust" again. Write two things you might find in an attic.

1. _____

2. _____

Think Ahead

Look at the title and pictures and read the first paragraph. Check the box next to the words that best finish the sentence below.

In this story, a boy finds something in the attic that

☐ is broken.

☐ means a lot to him.

☐ he can use in baseball.

Reading Fiction

Strategies:
QUESTION
MAKE INFERENCES
UNDERSTAND GENRE
VISUALIZE

QUESTION:
Remember to ask yourself questions as you read.

What does Mom mean when she says, "Our attic is full of memories"?

memory (MEM-uh-ree) something that is remembered

Early one morning, Marcus followed his mother up the stairway to the attic. Boxes, furniture, and old toys filled the room. "Our attic is full of memories," Mom said, "And once a memory is gone, it's gone forever."

Mom had promised Marcus a reward for writing a prize-winning story. His class was supposed to write a story about the past. There would be a prize for the best story.

"You can look through two boxes today, Marcus," Mom said, as she went off to another corner of the attic. Marcus was hoping to find a pack of baseball cards that his father had put away a long time ago. Maybe this would be his lucky day. He closed his eyes and picked two boxes.

The first one was filled with some old roller-skates. He opened the second box. There, on top, were some pictures of a beautiful young woman. He didn't know who she was, but under the pictures were some letters, books, and notebooks.

"Who is this, Mom?" he asked.

Mom stood over the box. "That's Grandma," Mom said.

"That doesn't look like Grandma," he said.

"She was young once, too," Mom laughed.

"Is this her journal?" Marcus asked, holding up a notebook.

Mom picked it up and looked inside. "Yes, this journal has some of Grandma's first stories."

Then Mom picked up another book. The cover said *Dust Tracks on a Road.* "This was one of Grandma's favorite books. It's by a writer named Zora Neale Hurston."

"Who?" Marcus asked.

"Zora Neale Hurston, an African-American woman who was born over 100 years ago," Mom said. "She was quite a writer—and quite a woman, too."

"What do you mean?" Marcus asked.

"It was almost impossible for an African American woman to become a writer in those days," Mom said. "You need to ask Grandma about her. She can tell you lots more than I can."

MAKE INFERENCES

You know that authors don't tell you everything. Instead they give you clues.

I know that most people in those days didn't go to school. I can tell Zora Neale Hurston did.

How can you tell Zora went to school? Check the box next to the clue.

☐ She could write.

☐ She was quite a woman.

☐ She was born over 100 years ago.

© 2002 Options Publishing Inc.

education
(ej-u-CAY-shun)
learning; schooling

That afternoon, Marcus walked into Grandma's apartment. "What do you have there?" Grandma asked.

Marcus held up the journal and the book he had found in the attic. Grandma's big eyes got even bigger as she smiled. "Zora Neale Hurston was my hero!" she exclaimed.

"Why was she your hero, Grandma?"

"Zora Neale Hurston lived quite a life," Grandma said. Her eyes flashed with excitement. "By the time she was 13, her mother had died and Zora was alone. Even so, she got an education and became a writer."

"That must've been hard," Marcus said.

"Very hard. After I read Zora's book about her life, I decided I could become a writer, too."

Marcus walked over to Grandma's bookcase. She had written most of the children's books on her shelf. Marcus was very proud of his grandma.

"I want to be a writer someday, too," he said. "You *can* be a writer," Grandma said. "You know what Zora Neale Hurston's mom used to tell her?"

"What?"

"She always said, 'Jump at de sun.' She meant that you can do whatever you set your mind on. So, Marcus, just remember that, and you, too, will get whatever *you* set your mind on."

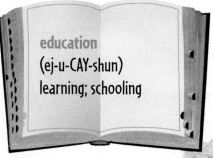

© 2002 Options Publishing Inc.

Attic Stardust

Visualize

Story settings help the reader get a picture of where and when a story takes place. Many stories can have more than one setting. This story has two. Fill in the setting webs below.

First Setting

_____

When (Time)

_____

Where (Place)

_____

Details (More Information)

_____

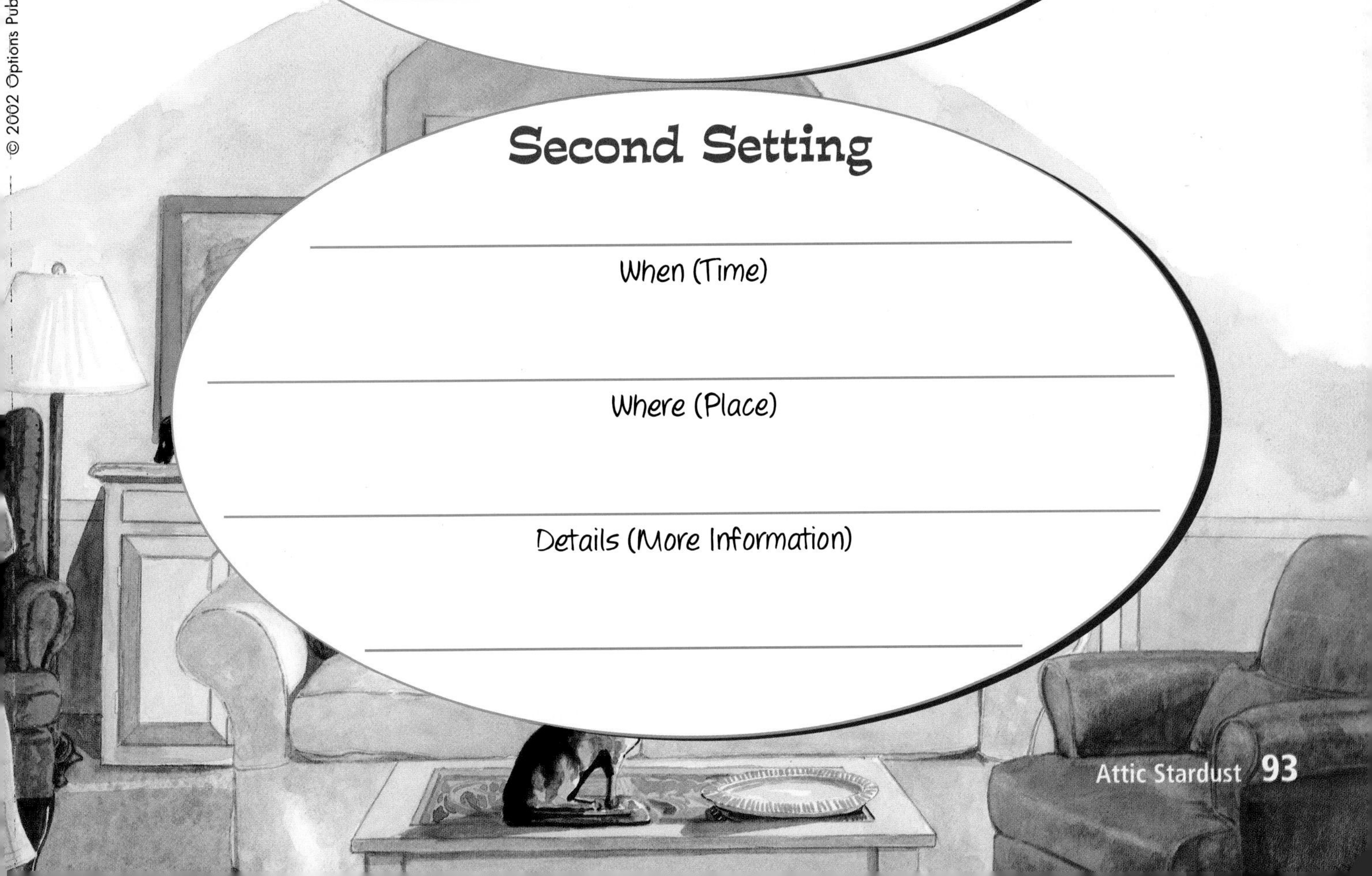

Second Setting

_____

When (Time)

_____

Where (Place)

_____

Details (More Information)

_____

Summarize

After you read a story, try to summarize it. That is a good way to see if you understand all the parts.

Write a short summary of "Attic Stardust." Use what you learned about the settings to help you summarize the story. Tell two things that happened in each setting.

First Setting: 1. _____

_____

2. _____

_____

Second Setting: 1. _____

_____

2. _____

_____

Determine What Is Important

Try to remember the most important ideas in a story. If you can remember the main ideas, you will be able to remember the details as well. Put a check next to two main ideas below.

__ Grandma told Marcus about Zora Neale Hurston.

__ Grandma had a bookshelf.

__ Marcus opened a box that had skates in it.

__ Marcus went to Grandma's in the afternoon.

__ Marcus learned a lot about Grandma's life.

Getting Ready

Why does a person become a writer? Read this biography to find out about one writer from Eatonville.

Zora Neale Hurston

Think About Genre

In "Attic Stardust," Mom and Grandma are made-up characters. However, they both tell facts about Zora Neale Hurston—a real person. This nonfiction story is a biography of Zora Neale Hurston. A biography tells the story of a real person's life.

Look through this biography. Look at the headings and pictures. Then answer **yes** or **no** to each of the following questions.

1. Does this biography tell about different parts of Zora Neale Hurston's life?

_____

2. Does it tell about her family?

_____

3. Does it tell about writers of the future?

_____

4. Does it show what she looked like?

_____

Think About the Topic

Remember what you read about Zora Neale Hurston in "Attic Stardust." Complete each sentence below.

1. What did you learn about her?

_____

_____

2. What would you like to learn?

_____

_____

Think Ahead

Look at the story headings again. Two headings tell you that Zora Neale Hurston had to work very hard during her life. Check the box next to each heading that helps you predict that her life was not easy.

☐ The Busy Hurston Home

☐ Early Struggles

☐ The Harlem Renaissance

☐ A Writer's Struggle

MAKE CONNECTIONS
Think about where you read "jump at de sun" before.

I read it in "Attic Stardust." Grandma explained it to Marcus.

What does Zora's mother mean when she tells Zora to "jump at de sun"?

_____

_____

_____

_____

defended (de-FEND-ed) Kept safe from harm

encouraged (en-KUR-ijd) gave hope to

spirit (SPIR-it) liveliness, courage

Zora Neale Hurston

The Busy Hurston Home

Born in 1891, Zora Neale Hurston was number seven of eight children. There were six boys and two girls. The Hurston home was always noisy. Friends and visitors were always around.

Zora's father was the mayor of their town, Eatonville, Florida. It was the first African-American town in America run by African-Americans. About 300 people lived there.

Zora's favorite spot in Eatonville was Joe Clark's store. Men gathered at the store to tell stories. Zora spent much time there listening. She learned a lot about storytelling.

Zora never got along with her father. He didn't like her spirit. She didn't always listen to him. He told her not to read books. She read everything in sight. He didn't like poets. She said she was going to be a poet one day.

But Zora's mother listened to her stories. She defended Zora. She encouraged her to "jump at de sun."

© 2002 Options Publishing Inc.

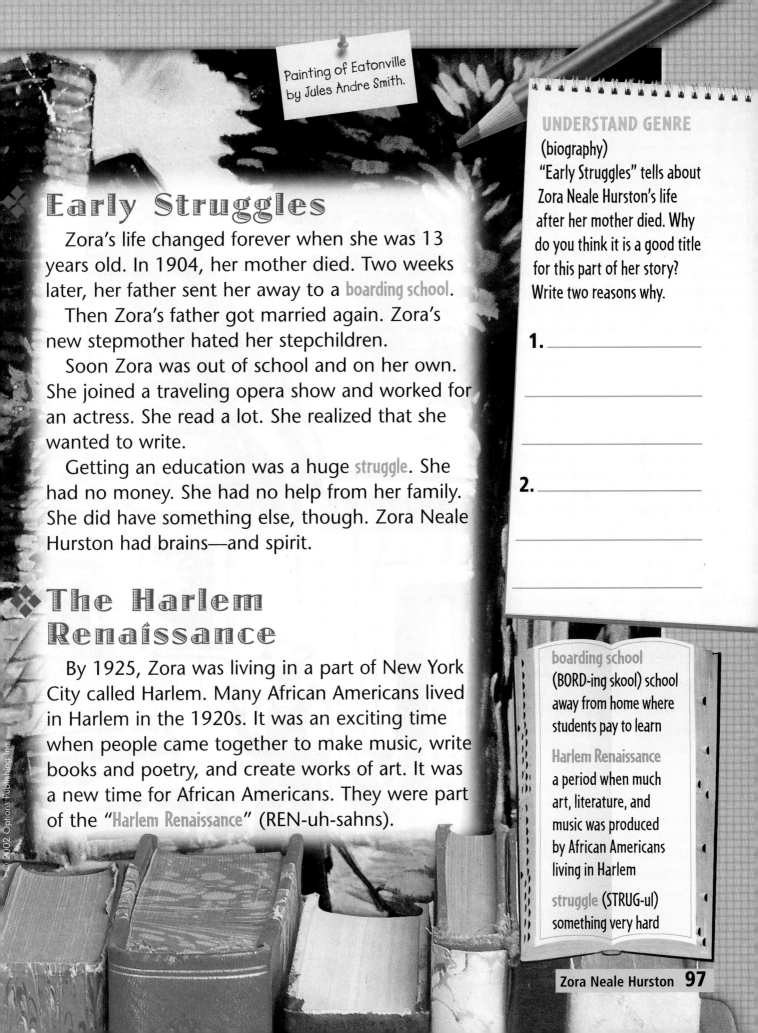

Painting of Eatonville by Jules Andre Smith.

Early Struggles

Zora's life changed forever when she was 13 years old. In 1904, her mother died. Two weeks later, her father sent her away to a boarding school.

Then Zora's father got married again. Zora's new stepmother hated her stepchildren.

Soon Zora was out of school and on her own. She joined a traveling opera show and worked for an actress. She read a lot. She realized that she wanted to write.

Getting an education was a huge struggle. She had no money. She had no help from her family. She did have something else, though. Zora Neale Hurston had brains—and spirit.

The Harlem Renaissance

By 1925, Zora was living in a part of New York City called Harlem. Many African Americans lived in Harlem in the 1920s. It was an exciting time when people came together to make music, write books and poetry, and create works of art. It was a new time for African Americans. They were part of the "Harlem Renaissance" (REN-uh-sahns).

UNDERSTAND GENRE
(biography)
"Early Struggles" tells about Zora Neale Hurston's life after her mother died. Why do you think it is a good title for this part of her story? Write two reasons why.

1._____

_____

_____

2._____

_____

_____

boarding school
(BORD-ing skool) school away from home where students pay to learn

Harlem Renaissance
a period when much art, literature, and music was produced by African Americans living in Harlem

struggle (STRUG-ul) something very hard

© 2002 Options Publishing Inc.

Zora struggled her whole life to earn a living. She earned some fame, but she never made much money.

Many times she worked at different jobs. She worked as a waitress. She worked in a library. She taught. She cleaned houses.

Through it all, Zora wrote and traveled. She published many books, short stories, and plays. She had a lot to say about the lives of African Americans.

Zora Neale Hurston died in 1960. Her life was hard, but she always tried to "jump at de sun."

QUESTION

Ask yourself questions about titles or explanations on photographs and charts.

Choose one "Star" of the Harlem Renaissance. What would you want to know about him or her? Write your question below.

_____

_____

_____

_____

_____

_____

Stars of the Harlem Renaissance

 ▶ **Bessie Smith**

 ▶ **Langston Hughes**

 ▶ **Duke Ellington**

fame (FAYM) the condition of being well-known; popular

Zora Neale Hurston

50 SEPIAN

DINNER

Visualize

This biography is written in time order. It starts when Zora is a child and ends when she dies.

The graphic organizer below is a time line. It shows the time order of events.

Write an event in each "event" box. Then look back at the headings in the biography to help you figure out when things happened. Write each event or the date it happened in a box.

Major events in Zora Neale Hurston's life.

Event	Event	Event	Event
Zora is born.			

Date	Date	Date	Date
1891			1960

Zora Neale Hurston

Summarize

Your friends may not know about Zora Neale Hurston. What important things would you tell them about her?

Write a summary about her life. Include dates and events from the time line on page 99.

_____

_____

_____

_____

_____

Determine What Is Important

Almost everything we write has important ideas and details. Important ideas are explained or supported by details. Choose one detail that explains or supports each important idea below. Fill in the bubble next to it.

1. Zora worked at different jobs.

   Ⓐ Sometimes she worked as a waitress or a teacher.

   Ⓑ Zora wrote and liked to travel.

2. Many talented people were part of the Harlem Renaissance.

   Ⓐ Some singers lived in New York City.

   Ⓑ Writers, singers, and poets came together in Harlem in the 1920s.

WRITINGS BY ZORA NEALE HURSTON FROM THE FEDERAL WRITERS' PROJECT

go Gator and muddy the Water

Edited and with a Biographical Essay by PAMELA BORDELON

Many of Zora Neale Hurston's books are widely read today.

Attic Stardust

Zora Neale Hurston

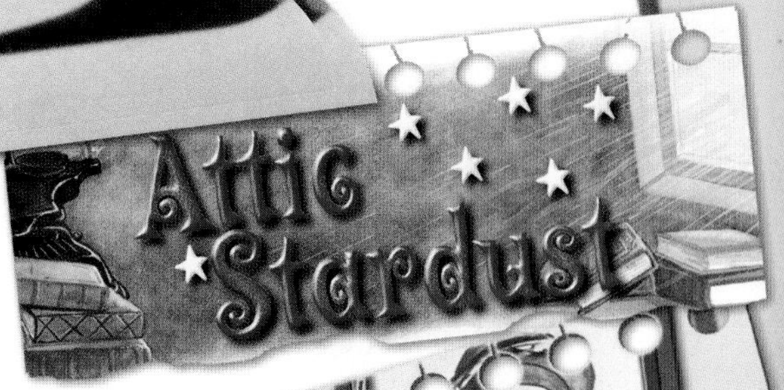

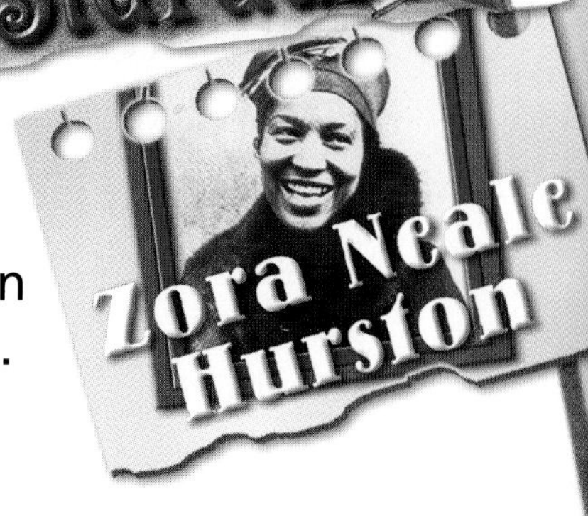

Make Connections

Think of what you learned about Zora Neale Hurston in both selections.

1. In "Attic Stardust," Grandma called Zora Neale Hurston her hero. Write about someone you think is your hero. Tell why.

2. How do you think Marcus, the boy in "Attic Stardust," would feel after reading the biography "Zora Neale Hurston"?

3. What kind of person do you think Zora Neale Hurston was?

4. If you could meet Zora Neale Hurston, what would you like to ask her about her life?

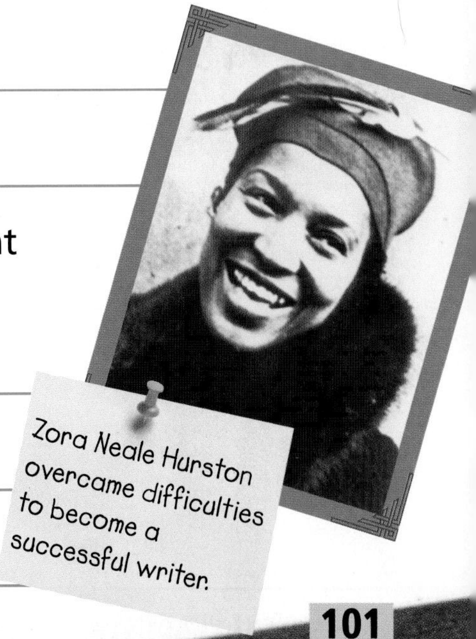

Zora Neale Hurston overcame difficulties to become a successful writer.

Attic Stardust

Zora Neale Hurston

Write Interview Questions

Writers sometimes interview people before they write a biography. Choose a classmate or family member you would like to interview. Think of some questions you would like to ask about the person's life. Write three questions and try them out on someone.

1. _____

2. _____

3. _____

BLACKLINE MASTER Before you write, use the Blackline Master your teacher will give you to help you think of good questions.

Plan Your Research

Choose one "star" from page 98. Write three things you would like to learn about him or her.

1. _____

_____

2. _____

_____

3. _____

_____

The writer Langston Hughes was a friend of Zora Neale Hurston.

Net Connection

http://www.si.umich.edu/CHICO/Harlem/text/harlemwriters.html

A Mammoth Adventure

By studying their ancient bones, scientists have learned a lot about huge furry beasts that once lived on the earth. We call them mammoths. These gigantic animals died out thousands of years ago. Could someone living today ever hope to see one—alive?

Think About Genre

Fantasy stories are make-believe. Things happen in fantasies that could never happen in real life. Some fantasy stories, though, have parts that *seem* real. The characters may seem just like real people. The place may be a real place. So, how do you know if a story is a fantasy? Just ask yourself, "Could these things really happen?" If not, you know the story is a fantasy.

Think about a fantasy story you have heard or read. Write its title on line 1. On line 2, write one thing that happened in the story that could not happen in real life.

1. _____

_____

2. _____

_____

Think About the Topic

Read the introduction to "A Mammoth Adventure" again. What does it tell you about mammoths? Write two facts on the lines below.

1. _____

2. _____

Think Ahead

Titles can give you clues to the kind of story you will read. What kind of adventure do you think the children in the story will have?

_____

Strategies:
QUESTION
VISUALIZE
UNDERSTAND GENRE
MAKE INFERENCES

A Mammoth Adventure

QUESTION
Remember to ask yourself questions about the story.

I wonder why Liz and Ray are visiting Hot Springs, South Dakota?

What is the "real thing" they might find in Hot Springs?

"Wow!" said Liz, looking up at a huge skeleton. "Don't you wish you could see the real thing?"

"That's why I begged mom to bring us here," said Ray. "I've always wanted to see a real mammoth. Too bad they are extinct."

Liz and Ray were at a museum in Hot Springs, South Dakota. The trip was Ray's idea. He was writing a school report about mammoths. Many mammoth bones have been found in Hot Springs.

"There used to be a very big pool of hot water here," Ray told his sister. "The water was warm all year round. Animals came to the pool to drink, but they couldn't get out. The sides were too steep. It was a death trap!"

"Where is the water now?" asked Liz.

extinct (ek STINGKT) no longer living anywhere in the world

steep (STEEP) slant sharply

© 2002 Options Publishing Inc.

"Long gone!" said Ray. "The pool slowly filled up with dirt. The bones of the trapped animals were hidden under all that dirt for 26,000 years! Now people are beginning to dig them out."

Later, Ray showed Liz a poster he was making for his school project. On it was a time line and a pointer.

"This is a time line chart," he explained. "It shows what happened to the mammoths through the years."

"Oh, here's when the mammoths died in the pool," said Liz as she moved the pointer to 26,000 years ago. Ray had put a mammoth sticker there to mark it.

As soon as the pointer touched the sticker, something very strange happened. The sticker seemed to come alive! Suddenly there was a rush of cold wind. Then, the museum disappeared! Ray and Liz were now standing on a grassy hill! And there were patches of snow on the ground!

As they turned, they saw a gigantic hairy beast. It looked like an elephant, but it had long brown fur and huge sharp tusks that were curved at the ends.

Liz and Ray backed away very slowly.

"Luckily, w-w-woolly mammoths d-d-don't eat m-m-meat!" stammered Ray.

VISUALIZE
Words can help you picture something in your mind. Which words help you "see" what's happening in the story?

tusks (TUSKS) very long, pointed teeth of animals like the elephant

UNDERSTAND GENRE
(time-travel fantasy)
This story has parts that seem real and parts that are fantasy. Write one example of each.

Real: _____

_____

_____

Fantasy: _____

_____

MAKE INFERENCES

Why did Ray draw a line in the snow? Circle the letter of the correct answer.

a. to separate them from the bear
b. to make a time line to get them back to the present
c. to explain to Liz where they were

Ice Age (IYS ayj)
a time long ago when most of Earth was covered with ice

"Where are we?" asked Liz.

"We must have traveled back in time to the **Ice Age**," said Ray. "I guess my wish came true. I'm seeing a real mammoth!"

Suddenly Liz looked really scared. All she could do was point at an animal coming over the snowy hill.

"Oh, no!" yelled Ray. "That giant bear definitely is a meat eater!"

"And it's coming this way!"cried Liz.

Quickly, Ray picked up a stick and drew a line in the snow. He pulled Liz onto the line with him. Then, as fast as he could, Ray wrote the word NOW where the line ended. Just in time! There was another rush of wind.

"Oh, there you are!" said their mother. "For a minute, I thought you two had disappeared."

Ray felt dizzy. He and Liz were in a motel in Hot Springs. As his mother left the room, Ray stared at his poster.

"Should we tell her?" asked Liz.

"No way," said Ray. "Who would ever believe a crazy story like that?"

Visualize

A Mammoth Adventure

In a time-travel story, the setting is very important. Go back through the story. The setting changes a few times. Find each change. Then fill in the story map below. Describe where and when each part of the story happened. The last setting is almost the same as one of the other settings.

Beginning [Setting 1:]

Where?: _Museum in Hot Springs, SD_

When?: _Present_

What happened?: _____

Middle [Setting 2:]

Where?: _Ice Age_

When?: _____

What happened?: _____

End [Setting 3:]

Where?: _____

When?: _____

What happened?: _____

Summarize

Finish each sentence below to create a summary of the story. Use the story map on page 107 to help you.

The title of the story is _____ .

The main characters are _____ and _____ .

At first, we meet them in _____ .

Suddenly, they are in a _____ .

They see a _____ and a _____ .

Finally, they are in a _____ with their mother.

Determine What Is Important

Read the five statements below. Decide which two statements are the most important. Fill in the bubbles next to each one. Check to see if you included this information in your summary.

Ⓐ Ray showed Liz the poster he was making for a school project.

Ⓑ Ray and Liz were visiting a museum in Hot Springs, South Dakota, to see mammoth bones.

Ⓒ Long ago, there was a pool at Hot Springs, South Dakota.

Ⓓ Ray knew that mammoths were not meat eaters.

Ⓔ Ray and Liz traveled back to the time of the mammoths.

Getting Ready

The frozen body of a woolly mammoth lay hidden in the ground for more than 20,000 years. Then, in 1997, one of its tusks was seen sticking up out of the ice! What can scientists learn from this amazing find?

Frozen in Time

Think About Genre

Look at the pages of this informational article. Then read each statement below. Fill in the bubble next to each statement that you think describes this selection.

Ⓐ It gives information.

Ⓑ It is a fantasy story.

Ⓒ It is mostly about people who lived long ago.

Ⓓ It tells about things that really happened.

Think About the Topic

Read the introduction to "Frozen in Time" again. Ask yourself: *What do I already know about mammoths?* Write two things you know on the lines below.

1. _____

_____

2. _____

_____

Think Ahead

Take a quick look at the article. Then tell what you think you will learn when you read "Frozen in Time."

_____

_____

Early humans used mammoth bones and furs to make shelters.

Reading Nonfiction

Strategies:

MAKE INFERENCES
UNDERSTAND GENRE
MAKE CONNECTIONS

Frozen in Time

A Strange Discovery

An enormous tusk was sticking out of the snow in Siberia, a part of Russia. The tusk was still attached to the frozen body of an ancient woolly mammoth. The mammoth's body was buried in the cold, hard ground.

The men who first found the tusk in 1997 removed it from the body. Then they dug up the other tusk. They took the tusks to a market to sell them.

There they met Bernard Buigues (BWEEG), a French explorer. He was interested in the tusks. But he was even more interested in the mammoth they came from. The men agreed to take him to the body.

Bernard Buigues was very excited by what he saw. Usually, scientists have only mammoth bones and teeth to study. This mammoth still had flesh and hair! The body had been preserved in ice for more than 20,000 years.

MAKE INFERENCES

Remember to use the clues an author gives you to figure things out.

Bernard Buigues is an explorer, not a scientist. Why do you think he wants to see the mammoth?

Fill in the bubble next to your answer.

Ⓐ He is curious about what the mammoth looks like.

Ⓑ He likes digging in the ice.

Ⓒ He wants to sell the rest of the mammoth.

---

flesh (FLESH) the soft part of the body that covers the bones

preserved (prih ZERVD) kept from rotting or spoiling

A scientist examines 23,000-year-old mammoth teeth

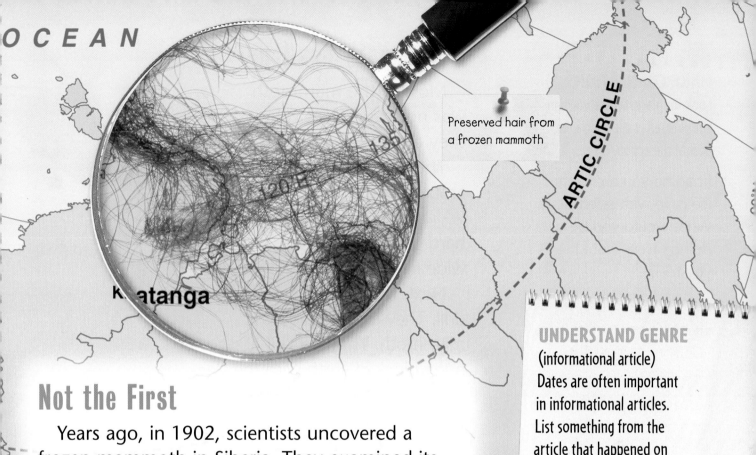

Preserved hair from a frozen mammoth

ARTIC CIRCLE

OCEAN

Khatanga

Not the First

Years ago, in 1902, scientists uncovered a frozen mammoth in Siberia. They examined its hair and skin. They even found out what it ate. More than 30 pounds of grass and other plants were still in its stomach!

Scientists at the time did not have the tools they have today. They used hot water to melt the frozen ground around the mammoth. As they uncovered the body, it began to rot. Not much was left for scientists to study.

Return to Siberia

In 1999, a team of scientists went back to Siberia to study a mammoth that had just been discovered. The problem was, they could not study it where it was found. The ground was as hard as rock and the weather was very windy and extremely cold.

About 150 miles away, there was a big ice cave in the town of Khatanga. If the scientists could get the mammoth to the ice cave, they could study it there. But how do you move a frozen mammoth?

UNDERSTAND GENRE
(informational article)
Dates are often important in informational articles. List something from the article that happened on each of these dates.

1902 _____

_____

_____

_____

1999 _____

_____

_____

A Mammoth Challenge

Moving the mammoth was not easy! Here is how they did it.

The first step was to dig all around it. They used two big jackhammers to cut through the hard ground. They dug a deep, wide trench.

Next, they used a large drill. They drilled under the mammoth. They cut out a huge block of earth with the mammoth inside. Then they built a strong cage around it.

Finally, it was time for the helicopter to lift it out of the ground. The helicopter was huge. But would it be strong enough? The block weighed 23 tons!

The men hooked the block to the helicopter. The helicopter rose, slowly lifting the block into the air. The mammoth was on its way to Khatanga!

Lifting the ice block with the frozen mammoth was a dangerous operation.

Working in an Ice Cave

The ice cave was a cold place to work. It had to be! The only way to preserve the mammoth was to keep it frozen.

The work was very slow. Scientists used hair dryers to melt one tiny piece of the block at a time. This discovery would help them learn what the world was like when mammoths walked the earth.

challenge
(CHAL-inj) something that is hard to do

jackhammers
(JAK-ham-erz) high-powered drills used to break up rock or pavement

trench (TRENCH) a deep path cut in the earth

Visualize

"Frozen in Time" tells about a problem and the steps taken to solve the problem. Look for the problem in the part called "Return to Siberia." Write it below. Find how scientists solved it in the part "A Mammoth Challenge." List the steps below.

Problem

_____

Solution

Step 1: _____

_____

Step 2: _____

_____

Step 3: _____

_____

Step 4: _____

_____

Frozen in Time

Summarize

Summarize "Frozen in Time" by answering each of the following questions.

1. *What was discovered?*
2. *What do scientists want to do with it?*
3. *What was the biggest problem they faced?*
4. *How did they solve the problem?*

Write your summary on the lines below. Read it to a friend when you are finished.

1. _____

2. _____

3. _____

4. _____

Determine What Is Important

You can often pick out important facts by asking *What? Where? Who? When?* and *Why?*

Write an important fact from the article that answers each question below.

Mammoth tusks could be as long as 17 feet.

<u>What</u> was found in 1997? _____

<u>Where</u> was it found? _____

<u>Who</u> came to study it? _____

<u>When</u> did the scientists return to dig it out? _____

<u>Why</u> did they need to move it? _____

Make Connections

Think about the two selections you just read. Do they remind you of other information you have read, heard, or seen somewhere?

1. Does the mammoth remind you of any animal that you know? Which one? Tell how that animal is like a woolly mammoth and how it is different.

Animal: _____

Like a mammoth: _____

Different from a mammoth: _____

2. Scientists in "Frozen in Time" are slowly uncovering a frozen mammoth. When they are finished, what will the mammoth look like? Use details from "A Mammoth Adventure."

_____

_____

_____

3. Ray, like real scientists, wants to learn about animals that lived long ago. Are you interested in such animals? Tell why or why not.

_____

_____

_____

115

Write a Friendly Invitation

What if you really could travel back in time? Write an invitation to a friend or relative. Tell where you would be going and when you would be leaving. Give reasons why you think it would be a great trip.

Dear _____

Please come on a time-travel trip with me!

Where: _____

When: _____

Why: _____

Hope you'll join me! It will be fun!

BLACKLINE MASTER Before you write, use the Blackline Master your teacher will give you to plan your invitation.

Plan Your Research

What else would you like to learn about mammoths or other Ice Age animals? What questions do you have about these animals? Write two questions that you would like to have answered.

1. _____

2. _____

_____

Net Connection

http://www.mammothsite.com/index.html

http://www.discovery.com/exp/mammoth/mammoth.html

Getting Ready

Sunlight and Fire

**How could a rabbit and a coyote help people out?
Find out in these two folktales. They were told by the Paiute (PIE-yoot)
Indians of the American West.**

Think About Genre

Folktales are stories that people have told for many years. No one knows who first told the story. People passed folktales on from one teller to the next. It may be hundreds of years before they are written down.

Myths are special folktales. They are made-up stories that tell about things in nature. Myths may explain how things first began.

Fill in the bubble next to each statement that describes a myth. There are two.

Ⓐ It tells of a time long ago.

Ⓑ All characters dress like people you know.

Ⓒ It explains something in nature and how it first began.

Ⓓ It has facts you can check.

Think About the Topic

Think about the titles "Sunlight" and "Fire." Ask yourself: *Why are sunlight and fire important?* Complete each sentence.

Sunlight is important because:

_____

Fire is important because:

_____

Think Ahead

Read the title and introduction again. Take a quick look at the stories. What great things do you think rabbit and coyote will do?

Rabbit: _____

Coyote: _____

Fiction

Strategies:
MAKE INFERENCES
MAKE CONNECTIONS
UNDERSTAND GENRE

Sunlight and Fire

Sunlight

A long time ago, there were not many hours of daylight. Days were very short. The Paiute people did not have enough time to hunt. The rabbit Tavu wanted to help so he decided to go to the place where daylight began. He packed up his arrows and set out on a **journey** east, toward the sun.

Tavu traveled far. At last he came to the edge of the world, where the sun lived. He hid behind some rocks and waited.

As soon as the sun began to rise, Tavu raised his arrow, took aim, and shot it. The arrow quickly burned up before it reached the sun. Tavu tried again. He walked closer to the sun, shooting arrows as he went. Every arrow burst into flames before it reached its mark.

Finally, there were only two arrows left. Tavu began to **weep**. He cried so much that his tears caused his last two arrows to become soaking wet. He took aim again and shot the first of those two arrows. Tavu smiled. It almost hit the sun!

Then Tavu let his last arrow fly. This time, the arrow hit! The sun fell to the ground.

MAKE INFERENCES

Authors do not tell you everything. They depend upon the things they think you already know to help you understand what they are saying.

> I know the sun rises in the East, so that's why the author has Tavu travel East.

Think about Tavu's tears. Why do you think they were able to keep the arrows from burning up?

---

journey (JUR-ne) a long trip

weep (WEEP) cry

Quickly, Tavu cut the sun into pieces. He threw one piece into the sky.

"Go higher and make the days longer," he commanded. Then he ran away as fast as he could.

Every time the angry sun tried to chase Tavu, Tavu hid. At last the sun gave up. Tavu watched it move higher and higher into the sky. He was very pleased. "Now the day will be long enough," he said.

When Tavu returned, the people celebrated. They held a big sun dance. Then they asked Tavu to do even more.

"Go fight the sun again," they begged. "We want daylight all the time."

"No," said Tavu. "You need night as well as day. You need time for sleeping."

And from that day to this, it has been so.

Fire

A long time ago, the Paiute people had no fire. They were cold and miserable all winter long. Finally, a boy decided to do something about it. He went to Coyote to ask for his help.

MAKE CONNECTIONS
You read "Sunlight" and the beginning of "Fire." Both are Paiute myths. Think of what you know about myths and when they happened.

How are the story beginnings alike?

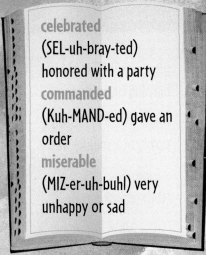

celebrated
(SEL-uh-bray-ted) honored with a party
commanded
(Kuh-MAND-ed) gave an order
miserable
(MIZ-er-uh-buhl) very unhappy or sad

In Native American Indian myths, animals often help people. The Paiute told myths about the rabbit and the coyote. Even though they are different animals, each one helped the Paiute in its own way.

What can you say about how both rabbit and coyote helped the Paiute? Fill in the bubble next to your answer.

(A) They were brave.

(B) They made things change.

(C) They solved problems.

Coyote knew where to get fire. "We must go west to the Burning Mountain," he said. "But," he warned, "it is very **dangerous**. We will need many fast runners."

The boy told his people. Soon all the best runners were ready. Coyote led the way.

They walked for many days. Every night, they stopped to leave one runner behind. There he would wait.

Soon, only the boy and Coyote were left. And then even Coyote was on his own. He **crept** slowly up to the place where the Fire Spirits lived. He waited patiently for the chance to steal a **blazing** piece of wood. It did not take long. He grabbed the wood and ran as fast as he could. The angry Fire Spirits chased him to where he was going. The boy stood waiting below.

Coyote passed the burning wood to the boy. The boy ran until he came to the next runner, who ran to the next. In this way, the fire passed from runner to runner and the Fire Spirits could not catch up to the runners.

Now the people had fire for cooking and heat. From then on, Coyote was called the Fire Bringer.

blazing (BLAZ-ing) burning or on fire

crept (KREPT) moved slowly in a sneaky way

dangerous (DAN-jer-us) unsafe

Visualize

The two stories you have read are alike
in many ways. Use the chart below to
help you compare them. Read the questions. Then look back
over each myth one at a time. Write answers in the chart.

"Sunlight" and "Fire": Two Paiute Myths

	Sunlight	Fire
1. When does the story take place?		
2. What problem did the people have?		
3. What animal helped them?		
4. How did the animal help?		
5. What changed for the people?		

Summarize

A good way to summarize these
two myths is to tell briefly how
they are alike. Use the information
in your chart on page 121 to help you.

_____

_____

_____

_____

_____

_____

Determine What Is Important

To remember these myths, you should recall the most important parts. Read each pair of
sentences below. In each pair, one sentence is more important. Fill in the bubble beside
that sentence.

Ⓐ Tavu shot the sun with an arrow.
Ⓑ Tavu's friends held a dance.

Ⓒ Coyote helped people get fire.
Ⓓ Coyote passed the fire to a boy.

Ⓔ Burning Mountain was in the West.
Ⓕ The people had no fire.

Getting Ready

Sarah Winnemucca

In the 1800s, the Paiute people needed a real-life hero. Sarah Winnemucca (wihn uh MUHK uh), the daughter of a Paiute leader, had a special skill with words. Could she, like Tavu and Coyote, help her people?

Think About Genre

The two myths you read told about brave animals who helped the Paiute people. Next you will read a biography about a real Paiute woman. You've read biographies of George Washington and Zora Neale Hurston. Biographies are different from myths. Write two things you would find in a biography but not in a myth.

1. _____

_____

2. _____

_____

The pinyon pine cone produced pine nuts, which were very valuable to the Paiute diet.

Think About the Topic

Reread the introduction to "Sarah Winnemucca." Ask yourself: *What does it tell me about her?* Write three ideas on the lines below.

1. _____

2. _____

3. _____

Think Ahead

Look at the title, art and time line in the biography. Write one question you think it will answer.

_____

_____

Sarah Winnemucca

QUESTION
Remember to ask yourself questions while you are reading.

I wonder why there were fewer animals to hunt. I guess the strangers did a lot of hunting, too.

The Paiute wanted to "drive" the strangers out of their land. What do you think "drive" means here?

_____

_____

_____

scarce (SKAIRS) hard to get; not much

survive (sur-VIVE) go on, stay alive

Sarah Winnemucca was a Paiute Indian. She was born in 1844 in what is now the state of Nevada. Her Paiute name was Thocmetony (THOCK-ma-toe-ne), which means "shell flower."

When Thocmetony was small, her family traveled from place to place to find food. They fished and hunted. They gathered pine nuts. Food was scarce in their land, but they had enough to eat.

Soon the Paiute way of life began to change. Strangers came into Paiute land. They brought cattle with them. They cut down trees. Now there were fewer pine nuts to gather. There were fewer animals to hunt. Life became difficult.

Many Paiutes wanted to fight. They wanted to drive the strangers out of their land. Thocmetony's grandfather, Truckee, (TRUHK ee) had a different idea. He believed that these strangers were brothers to the Paiute.

He believed that the only way the Paiute could survive was to learn to live together.

© 2002 Options Publishing Inc.

Time Line of Sarah Winnemucca's Life

	Makes first trip to California	Goes to girls' school in California for 3 weeks	Becomes an interpreter
Born			
1840	**1850**		**1860**

Thocmetony was afraid of the white strangers. In 1850, when she was six, Truckee decided to take her to California. He wanted her to meet these people and see how they lived. In California, she met many good people. She learned to be less afraid.

Truckee wanted his grandchildren to learn the ways of other people. Thocmetony began to learn English. She was given the name of Sarah.

When Sarah was 13, she and her sister, Elma, went to live with a white family in Nevada. They learned to speak and write in English. Sarah was a quick learner. She had a special gift for language.

Meanwhile, life for the Paiute became worse. More and more strangers came. They took away Paiute land and food. Sometimes they killed Paiute people for no reason.

Sarah knew she must do something. She began to fight for her people with the only weapon she had. She began to use her skill with words.

VISUALIZE

If we can "see" the story in our mind, we might remember it better.

Picture what Thocmetony looked like when she first arrived in California. What would the local people have seen when they looked at her?

_____

_____

_____

_____

weapon (WEP-un) something used in fighting

Goes to Washington, D.C. | Marries Lewis H. Hopkins | Publishes her book, Life Among the Piutes | Starts a school | Dies

1870   1880   1890   1900

A person's life has many, many events. An author has to choose just a few of those events for a short biography such as this one. Write down one event in Sarah Winnemucca's life. Tell why you think the author decided to include it.

_____

_____

_____

_____

_____

_____

_____

beliefs (bee-LEEFS) a feeling that something is real

goals (GOLZ) what you want, aim for in life

interpreter (in-TER-pruh-ter) a person who explains what words mean from one language to another

Everyone in the United States knew that there were problems between Native American Indians and others. Most people had heard only one side of the story. Sarah wanted them to learn the Native American Indian side, too.

Sarah worked as an interpreter. She wrote letters in English to important people. She explained Paiute beliefs in English so others could understand Indian life. Sarah discovered that people listened to her when she wore her native costume. They would come to the theater to see her up on the stage sharing stories about her people.

In 1880, Sarah went to Washington, D.C., to meet with the President of the United States. In 1883, she wrote a book about her people and their ways. It was the first book written by a Native American Indian woman.

Sarah had many hopes for her people. She did not reach all her goals. Yet the work she did was very important. She helped to build a bridge of understanding between two very different ways of life.

Sarah dressed in her beautiful native costume.

Understanding Nonfiction

Visualize

The author tells about Sarah Winnemucca's life through three main ideas. Other facts in the biography give you information about those main ideas.

Read each main idea in the chart below. Then read through the biography to find two facts that tell about each idea. Write one fact in each box under the main idea. Write the page you found it on.

Main Idea	**Main Idea:**	**Main Idea:**
The Paiute way of life changed when strangers came into their land.	Sarah learned the language and ways of strangers.	Sarah used words to help people understand each other.
Fact: Page: ____	**Fact:** Page: ____	**Fact:** Page: ____
Fact: Page: ____	**Fact:** Page: ____	**Fact:** Page: ____

Sarah Winnemucca

Summarize

One way to summarize a biography is by answering the questions about Who? When? Where? What? Why? and How? Answer these questions about "Sarah Winnemucca."

Who was Sarah Winnemucca? _____

When did she live? _____

Where did she live? _____

What was happening at that time? _____

_____

Why did Sarah move to California and Nevada? _____

_____

How did she "build a bridge of understanding"? _____

_____

Determine What Is Important

If you were given only one minute to tell about Sarah Winnemucca's life, you would have time to tell only the most important parts. Those are the parts that are needed to tell the story. Which facts below are important enough to be included in your one minute summary? Fill in the bubble next to three of the most important sentences.

Ⓐ Sarah's Paiute name, Thocmetony, is the name of a flower.

Ⓑ Sarah was very skillful in using the English language.

Ⓒ Pine nuts were an important food for Sarah's people.

Ⓓ Sarah's grandfather took her to California.

Ⓔ Sarah wrote a book to tell others about Paiute life.

Life among the Piutes
SARAH WINNEMUCCA HOPKINS

The book Sarah Winnemucca Hopkins wrote: Life Among the Piutes—Their Wrongs and Claims

Make Connections

Think about the two selections you have just read. Think of how they connect with each other and with other things you have seen or read.

1. These selections tell you many things about the Paiute Native American Indians. Write one thing you found interesting.

_____

_____

2. In what two ways was Sarah Winnemucca like Tavu and Coyote?

- _____

- _____

3. Think about a problem you have had with other people and how you helped to solve it.

Problem: _____

_____

_____

Solution: _____

_____

_____

Sunlight and Fire

Sarah Winnemucca

Write a Myth

Think about the two Paiute myths you have read. Use the space below to make some notes for a myth about a topic of your choosing. Remember to use elements that are common to myths, like animals for characters. Write your myth on a separate sheet of paper.

_____

_____

_____

_____

_____

BLACKLINE MASTER Before you write, use the Blackline Master your teacher will give you to plan your myth.

Beautiful Native American headdress used during ceremonies.

Plan Your Research

What else would you like to know about Native American Indians? Write two questions on the lines below.

1. _____

_____

2. _____

_____

Net Connection

http://www.si.umich.edu/chico/powwow

http://www.littlesioux.org/frmfamous.html

Getting Ready

This lesson is a test. After you read "Mystery on the Space Station," you will be asked questions about the reading. These questions will test how well you understand genre. They will also test how well you can use the reading strategies you have practiced: Determine What Is important, Summarize, Make Connections, Question, Make Inferences, and Visualize.

Strange things are happening on a space station. Something is missing and somebody has a secret. Can you solve the mystery?

Think About Genre

The selection you are going to read is a mystery. In this special kind of fiction, there is a mystery to be solved. The writer gives clues so that a good reader can try to solve the mystery before the characters do.

Which of the following would fit in a mystery? Put a check beside each one that fits. (There are two.)

☐ a detective

☐ graphs, maps, and tables

☐ funny jokes

☐ a stolen treasure

Think About the Topic

Read the introduction to "Mystery on the Space Station" again. Ask yourself: *What do I know about space travel? What do I know about space stations?* Write one thing you know about space travel or space stations.

_____

_____

Think Ahead

Look through the story. Think about what you know about space travel. What could be missing on a space station? What do you think "Mystery on the Space Station" will be about?

_____

_____

_____

astronaut (AS-truh-not) a person who goes into space

international (in-ter-NASH-uh-nuhl) from many countries

shuttle (SHUT-ul) space ship that goes back and forth between earth and space

e-Journal

Date: June 25, 2010

Time: late morning

Place: The ISS Space Shuttle

Willy Banks zipped up his space suit and looked out the window of the space **shuttle**. Then he sat down to wait for orders from his mother—Commander Rita Banks.

Commander Banks was in charge of the space shuttle. Soon she would be leading the crew of the **International** Space Station—or ISS, for short.

"Everybody strap in," Commander Banks ordered. "We will be docking in one hour."

Willy Banks locked in his seat straps. Then he lifted his backpack gently onto his lap. "Don't worry. We'll be there soon," he whispered.

Willy was excited. Today he would begin his stay on the ISS. He would be the first kid in history to live on the space station. He'd be on board for a whole summer.

His mother was an **astronaut** and a scientist. There would be five other astronauts, but Willy Banks would be the station's youngest member.

Willy looked out through the shuttle window again. The ISS was close now. The space station was as long as the football field at school. It was much bigger than any airplane or rocket ship he'd ever seen. And it would be "home" for the whole summer!

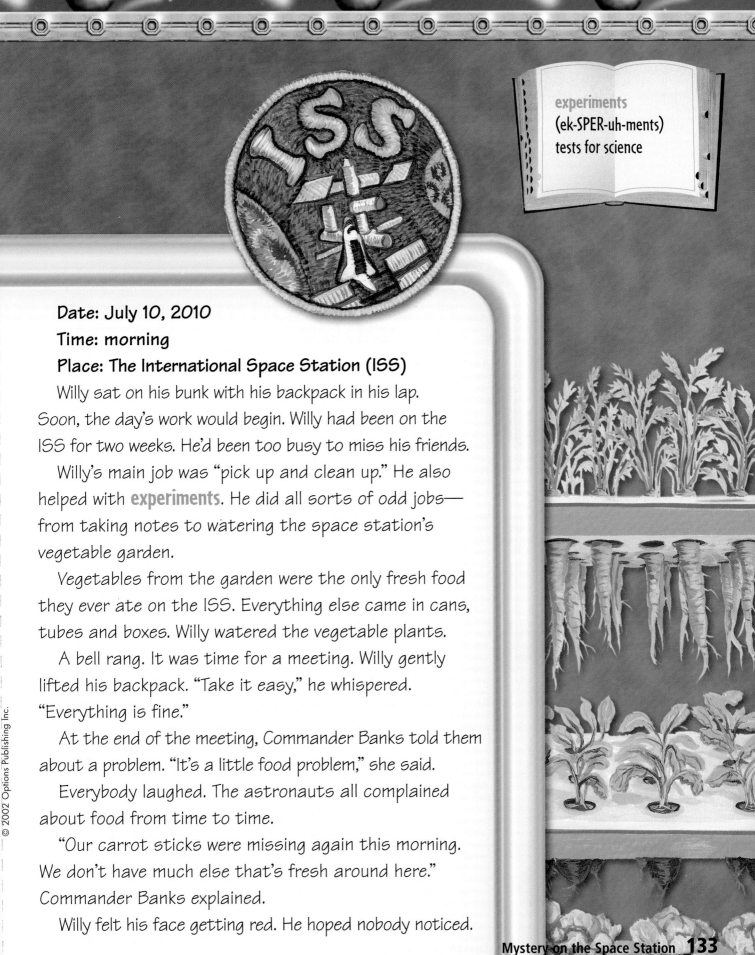

experiments
(ek-SPER-uh-ments)
tests for science

Date: July 10, 2010

Time: morning

Place: The International Space Station (ISS)

Willy sat on his bunk with his backpack in his lap. Soon, the day's work would begin. Willy had been on the ISS for two weeks. He'd been too busy to miss his friends.

Willy's main job was "pick up and clean up." He also helped with **experiments**. He did all sorts of odd jobs—from taking notes to watering the space station's vegetable garden.

Vegetables from the garden were the only fresh food they ever ate on the ISS. Everything else came in cans, tubes and boxes. Willy watered the vegetable plants.

A bell rang. It was time for a meeting. Willy gently lifted his backpack. "Take it easy," he whispered. "Everything is fine."

At the end of the meeting, Commander Banks told them about a problem. "It's a little food problem," she said.

Everybody laughed. The astronauts all complained about food from time to time.

"Our carrot sticks were missing again this morning. We don't have much else that's fresh around here." Commander Banks explained.

Willy felt his face getting red. He hoped nobody noticed.

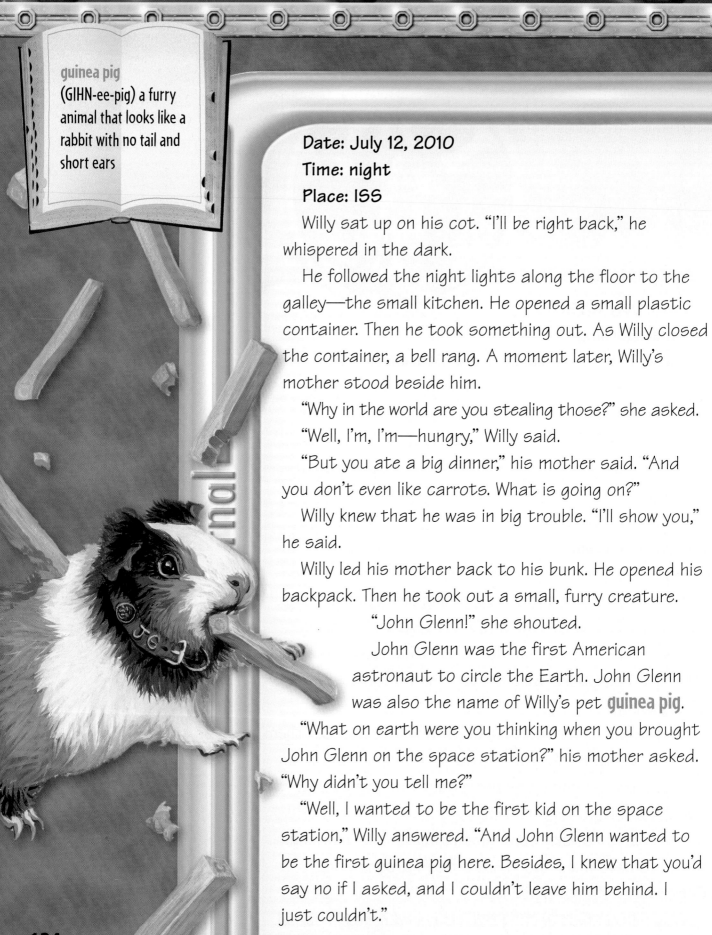

guinea pig
(GIHN-ee-pig) a furry animal that looks like a rabbit with no tail and short ears

Date: July 12, 2010
Time: night
Place: ISS

Willy sat up on his cot. "I'll be right back," he whispered in the dark.

He followed the night lights along the floor to the galley—the small kitchen. He opened a small plastic container. Then he took something out. As Willy closed the container, a bell rang. A moment later, Willy's mother stood beside him.

"Why in the world are you stealing those?" she asked.

"Well, I'm, I'm—hungry," Willy said.

"But you ate a big dinner," his mother said. "And you don't even like carrots. What is going on?"

Willy knew that he was in big trouble. "I'll show you," he said.

Willy led his mother back to his bunk. He opened his backpack. Then he took out a small, furry creature.

"John Glenn!" she shouted.

John Glenn was the first American astronaut to circle the Earth. John Glenn was also the name of Willy's pet **guinea pig.**

"What on earth were you thinking when you brought John Glenn on the space station?" his mother asked. "Why didn't you tell me?"

"Well, I wanted to be the first kid on the space station," Willy answered. "And John Glenn wanted to be the first guinea pig here. Besides, I knew that you'd say no if I asked, and I couldn't leave him behind. I just couldn't."

For numbers 1 through 6, use the strategies you have learned and fill in the letter of the sentence that best answers the question.

1. Why is there a vegetable garden on the space station? **(QUESTION STRATEGY)**

   Ⓐ so the astronauts have some fresh food

   Ⓑ for use in experiments

   Ⓒ so there is food for the guinea pig

   Ⓓ so Willy Banks has work for the summer

2. Willy whispers several times in the story. Why does he do this? **(MAKE INFERENCES STRATEGY)**

   Ⓐ He has to whisper in space.

   Ⓑ He has a weak voice.

   Ⓒ He doesn't want anybody to hear.

   Ⓓ He always talks to himself.

3. Why does Willy steal the carrot sticks? **(MAKE INFERENCES STRATEGY)**

   Ⓐ He never gets enough food at dinner.

   Ⓑ He needs carrots to feed his pet.

   Ⓒ He wants to throw them out.

   Ⓓ They are his favorite food.

4. Which of the following is a clue to the mystery of the missing carrots? **(UNDERSTAND GENRE STRATEGY)**

   Ⓐ Willy straps in his seat locks.

   Ⓑ Willy's job is "pick up and clean up."

   Ⓒ Willy lifts his backpack gently.

   Ⓓ Willy is too busy to miss his friends.

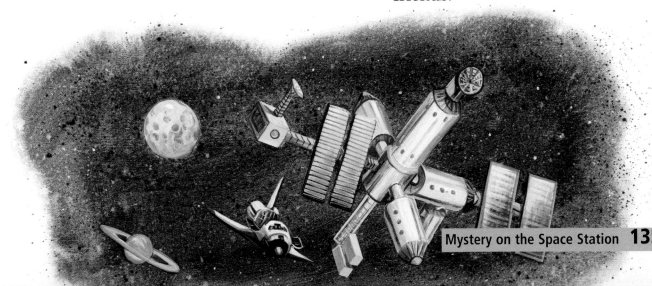

5. Willy can tell that the space station is bigger than any rocket. What other comparison does he make that helps you see the spaceship? **(VISUALIZE STRATEGY)**

Ⓐ It's bigger than a guinea pig.

Ⓑ It's taller than his school building.

Ⓒ It's as long as a football field.

Ⓓ It's as heavy as an elephant.

6. Which statement is most important in this mystery story? **(DETERMINE WHAT IS IMPORTANT STRATEGY)**

Ⓐ Willy does work on the ISS.

Ⓑ Commander Banks is in charge of the crew.

Ⓒ John Glenn is the name of an astronaut.

Ⓓ Willy has a secret.

For question 7, write a paragraph on the lines below.

7. Write a short summary. Tell what happened in "Mystery on the Space Station."
(DETERMINE WHAT IS IMPORTANT STRATEGY, SUMMARIZE STRATEGY)

_____

_____

_____

_____

_____

_____

_____

_____

STOP This is the end of the test for "Mystery on the Space Station." When your teacher tells you, go on to read the next selection, "Open House for the Space Station."

Getting Ready

Open House for the Space Station

This lesson is a test. After you read "Open House for the Space Station," you will be asked questions about the reading. These questions will test how well you understand genre. They will also test how well you can use the reading strategies you have practiced: Determine What Is Important, Summarize, Make Connections, Question, Make Inferences, and Visualize.

The International Space Station might sound like fiction. But it's really up there! Read all about it in this article.

Think About Genre

Most nonfiction has things that help the reader. Look through "Open House for the Space Station." Put a check next to each thing you see.

☐ photos or art that looks real

☐ headings that tell about each part

☐ maps, graphs, charts, or time lines

☐ directions for how to do something

Astronauts take a break to try some Japanese rice.

Think About the Topic

Reread the introduction. Think about "Mystery on the Space Station." Write two things that you now know about space stations.

1._____

_____

2._____

_____

Think Ahead

Think about the introduction and your preview. What do you think you will learn about in "Open House for the Space Station"?

_____

_____

Open House for the Space Station

About the International Space Station (ISS)

It will be as long as a football field. It will weigh almost one million pounds. But you won't be able to visit it anywhere on Earth. The International Space Station—or ISS—is being built *above* our planet.

Building the space station is a huge job. Sixteen countries are taking part. It will take five years to finish.

It all began in November, 1998. That's when the first module (MOJ-yool)—or piece—of the station was launched. At the end of the year 2000, the first crew went up for four months.

Looking Back at Space Station History

The ISS is not the first space station to be built. Russia's *Salyut 1* holds that record. But the ISS is the world's BIGGEST and BEST space station ever!

Look at this space-station time line.

The International Space Station (ISS) orbits above Earth.

crew (KROO) all the people working on a ship or plane

launched (lawncht) sent off

1971-1986

There were seven *Salyut* (sahl-YOOT) space stations in all. They were home to astronauts from over 10 countries. The longest stay was 237 days.

1973-1974

Skylab was America's first space station. It paved the way for research on the ISS.

© 2002 Options Publishing Inc.

What's for Dessert?

What does an astronaut eat on a space trip? A tube of meat paste? A bottle of bread goop? Or how about some sweet-potato ice cream?

Rupert Spies dreamed up this ice cream just for space. Spies is a chef. He's also part of a team that makes space foods. His team creates healthful, tasty foods for long space trips.

Food problems in space

On long trips, astronauts can bring only certain ingredients, and they can't visit a grocery store. So space food may be boring. But everybody has to eat!

What ingredients can they bring onto a space station? Melons, sweet potatoes, wheat, and peanuts make the list. But meat, milk, and cheese are out. Think about it: how would a cow fit on a spaceship? (And no cow, no milk.)

In space, stuffy noses are another problem. Without great smells, food doesn't taste as good. So astronauts may not enjoy eating.

Here's a third problem: astronauts are so busy, they sometimes forget to eat!

Now you can understand why food is a problem in space. Space chefs have to be problem solvers.

chef (SHEF) cook

ingredients (en-GREED-ee-yents) all of the things that go into a dish or food product

Ordinary healthy foods are allowed aboard the ISS.

1986–2001

Russia's *Mir* started circling Earth in 1986. Several American astronauts lived on *Mir*.

Russia's <u>Mir</u> has been orbiting the earth for 15 years!

Space Gardens

Space chefs have some ideas for better space food. They thought astronauts could grow veggies in space gardens. The ISS doesn't have much extra land. But a tiny garden would be worth every inch of land it uses. Healthful, fresh foods are good for everybody, even if you live in space!

Astronaut Scott J. Horowitz floats near the ceiling as he helps prepare a meal for the ISS crew.

drumstick (DRUM-stik) stick that is thick at one end and thin at the other

garlic (GAR-lik) small vegetable with strong flavor

patties (PAT-eez) small, flat cakes of food

What's for Dinner?

The recipe below was created for trips in space.

CARROT DRUMSTICKS

Ingredients

½ cup onions   ½ cup red peppers
½ cup mushrooms   2 teaspoons garlic
1 tablespoon vegetable oil   8 carrot sticks
1½ cups carrots, cooked and mashed
2 cups soft whole wheat bread crumbs
1 cup seasoned bread crumbs

To make the recipe:

✔ Fry onions, mushroom, peppers, and garlic in oil for 2 minutes.
✔ Combine the rest—except the dry bread crumbs and carrot sticks.
✔ Mix well. Form into eight drumstick patties.
✔ Roll the patties in bread crumbs.
✔ Bake at 350 degrees for 30 minutes.
✔ Put a carrot stick into one end of each baked patty.

Testing Your Understanding

For numbers 1 through 5, fill in the letter of the phrase or sentence that best answers the question.

1. The writer says the space station will take five years to finish. What other information helps you understand that this is a huge job? (MAKE CONNECTIONS STRATEGY)

   Ⓐ The first crew went up in 2000.

   Ⓑ They might grow a veggie garden.

   Ⓒ It started in November 1998.

   Ⓓ Sixteen countries are taking part.

2. The selection ends by telling how to do something. What does it tell how to do? (UNDERSTAND GENRE STRATEGY)

   Ⓐ how to build a space station

   Ⓑ how to make a space garden

   Ⓒ how to make carrot drumsticks

   Ⓓ how to become an astronaut

3. You might ask this question to test yourself: *What was the first space station?* Choose the best answer. (QUESTION STRATEGY)

   Ⓐ *Mir*

   Ⓑ *Salyut I*

   Ⓒ International Space Station

   Ⓓ *Skylab*

4. Here is another question you might ask to test yourself: *Why is space food a problem?* Read all the answers. Then choose the best answer. (QUESTION STRATEGY)

   Ⓐ Astronauts get stuffy noses.

   Ⓑ Space food can be boring.

   Ⓒ Astronauts forget to eat.

   Ⓓ All of the above.

5. Which sentence gives the most important idea of the story?
(DETERMINE WHAT IS IMPORTANT STRATEGY)

(A) The ISS is the biggest and best space station ever.

(B) The ISS is not the first space station.

(C) Carrot drumsticks are tasty and healthful.

(D) Russia sent up seven *Salyut* stations in all.

For question 6, write a paragraph on the lines below.

6. Write a short summary of "Open House for the Space Station." The headings in the article can help you decide what to include. (DETERMINE WHAT IS IMPORTANT STRATEGY, SUMMARIZE STRATEGY)

_____

_____

_____

_____

_____

_____

_____

_____

STOP This is the end of the test for "Open House for the Space Station." When your teacher tells you, continue on and finish the last part of the test.

Testing Your Understanding

For numbers 1 through 3, fill in the letter of the best answer. Look back at both selections if you need to. For number 4, write a few sentences.

1. How are the two selections alike? Choose the best answer. (MAKE CONNECTIONS STRATEGY)

   Ⓐ Both are about John Glenn.

   Ⓑ Both are about real things that happened on the International Space Station.

   Ⓒ Both are about the International Space Station.

   Ⓓ The two selections are both mysteries.

2. What happened in the mystery that has not happened yet in real life? (MAKE CONNECTIONS STRATEGY)

   Ⓐ Astronauts spent a long time in space.

   Ⓑ Men and women spent time in space.

   Ⓒ A boy spent time on a space station.

   Ⓓ Food on the space station was a problem.

3. What did you read about in both "Mystery on the Space Station" and "Open House for the Space Station"? (MAKE CONNECTIONS STRATEGY)

   Ⓐ The youngest astronaut ever was twelve.

   Ⓑ Food can be a problem for astronauts.

   Ⓒ All astronauts spend four months in space.

   Ⓓ Commander Rita Banks led the crew of the ISS.

4. How is life on a space station like life in another place you know, such as home, camp, or school? Write a few sentences on the lines below to answer this question. (MAKE CONNECTIONS STRATEGY)

   _____

   _____

   _____

   _____

5. Imagine that you are an astronaut who works on the International Space Station. Describe what you see and do there. Tell what the food is like. Help your readers picture life on the station. Include details from both selections.

_____

_____

_____

_____

_____

_____

_____

_____

_____

_____

_____

_____

STOP This is the end of the test.